ON THE OTHER SIDE
M**O**UNT
ARARAT

A story of a vanished city

ON THE OTHER SIDE
M OF OUNT
ARARAT

A story of a vanished city

Mariam Manoukian
Elize Manoukian

ABRIL PUBLISHING
Glendale, California

Library of Congress Control Number: 2005901694

ISBN: 0–9704131–7–3

Copyright © 2005 by Mariam Avakian Manoukian

MMG, Inc.
2500 Hospital Drive, Building 4
Mountain View, CA 94040

info@ontheothersideofMountArarat.com

www.ontheothersideofMountArarat.com

Armenia: EDIT PRINT Publishing House
          12-3 Toumanian St.
          Yerevan, Armenia, 375001

   USA: Abril Publishing
          415 E. Broadway Ave., Suite 102
          Glendale, CA 91205

10 9 8 7 6 5 4 3 2 1

This book is dedicated to three extraordinary Armenian women: Heranoush Beglarian, Elize Kardzair Manoukian and Irene Gyulnazarian

"I should like to see any power of the world destroy this race, this small tribe of unimportant people, whose wars have all been fought and lost, whose structures have been crumbled, literature is unread, music is unheard and prayers are no more answered. Go ahead, destroy Armenia. See if you can do it. Send them into the desert without bread or water. Burn their homes and churches. Then see if they will not laugh, sing or pray again. For when two of them meet anywhere in the world, see if they will not create a New Armenia."

—William Saroyan

CONTENTS

Part Seven
Farewell to Van
151

ACKNOWLEDGEMENTS

We are especially thankful to Dr. Rubina Peroomian, who is a long-time lecturer of Armenian Studies and currently Research Associate at UCLA, for taking the book seriously and putting her heart into it. She has done a tremendous work in checking the historic aspects of this novel, giving us priceless ideas and editorial corrections.

We would like to thank the following members of our family for unfailing support, valuable information and help while we were working on this project: Lena and Robert Avakian, Julie Beglarian, Sona Arabian, Vahan and Anoush Ajemian and Natasha Gonchar.

Above all, our thanks to Jerry and Gregory Manoukian for their love, hugs and support.

We would not be able to complete this novel without our dedicated team: Karen Hoxeng and Richard Kharibian who shaped the manuscript and brought it to life. We want to thank Karen Hoxeng for her editing talent, patience and professionalism at every step of the preparation and publishing of the book. We are grateful to Richard Kharibian for his masterful design and layout of the book, his meticulous work in creating the final look of the front and back cover, as well as designing the maps and the photos presented in the book.

We are indebted to Sona Arabian for her marvelous original artwork on the cover of this book.

We are grateful to Stina Katchadourian for her valuable critique at the early stages of the manuscript.

We would also like to thank Ruzanna Ohanjanian for generously offering us the unpublished priceless poetry (Autumn, Sunset and Frustration) of her talented daughter, Irene Gyulnazarian.

We also thank photographer Zaven Khachikian for the stunning photo of Mount Ararat, Dr. Aubrey Abramson for giving us the set of antique documents and books, and Janig Haleblian for providing us the photos of Van used for many descriptions presented in the book.

We take full responsibility and apologize for any remaining inaccuracies that might be found in the book.

PROLOGUE

"Into the soil of this beautiful and historic land, the Armenians have thrust deep roots. No brief civilization is theirs dating back to Mayflower or even Norman Conquest, but one that is almost coterminous with recorded history; and every Armenian feels behind him his vast antiquity, giving him personal dignity and great national pride."

—Hester Donaldson Jenkins
    "Armenia and Armenians," The National Geographic Magazine, October, 1915

This book depicts two years of life of one Armenian family in the city of Van, in the Ottoman Empire from 1913 to 1915. The city of Van sits on the shores of Lake Van, surrounded on the northwest by Mountain Sipan, and on the southwest Mount Nemrut. The highest peak on this land is Mount Ararat, the legendary resting place of Noah's Ark, situated in the northeast of Van.

Van has a long history and is probably one of the oldest cities in the world. As the Hittite annals show, civilization thrived in this area as early as the fourteenth century BC, but the first state in the area with an organized government was the Kingdom of Urartu, which reached its peak in the ninth century BC.

Around 834 BC, the Urartian King Sardouri I built his capital on the southeastern shore of Lake Van and called it Tushpa, or Tosp. Biainili was the name that Urartians called their kingdom, and that name later on gave rise to the Armenian name of the city—Van. In

782 BC, another Urartian king, Argishti II, founded the fortress of Erebuni in the eastern part of his kingdom. Over time, Erebuni evolved into modern Yerevan, capital of today's Armenia. The Kingdom of Urartu was known for its temples, fortresses and irrigation canals. Falling under barbaric attacks of the Assyrians and Medes, the Urartian Kingdom was able to continue its existence until the sixth century BC. Around 585 BC, Urartu fell, leaving numerous architectural sites and cuneiform writings. Urartu was no more, but throughout the land once ruled by Urartian Kings, the formation of the Armenian nation began to take shape through the commingling of diverse local and immigrant tribes. From the fifth century BC, the Persian and Greek sources referred to the country as Armenia and the people as Armenian. Through the centuries, Armenia had times of glory and times of darkness and foreign oppression, but Van was always the cradle of Armenian civilization.

At the height of its power, the Ancient Kingdom of Armenia consisted of 500,000 square miles of fertile land. In 94 BC, under Tigranes the Great, Armenia spread from the Black Sea to the Mediterranean Sea. Assyrians, Sasanid Persians, Romans, Arabs, Byzantines, Seljuks, Mongols, Tatars, Persian Safavids, Ottoman Turks and Russians make up a partial list of nations that either coexisted with Armenian Kingdoms or ruled the Armenians. The kingdom of Vaspurakan existed from the ninth until the eleventh Century. King Gagik Artsruni I built the Holy Cross Church on the Island of Akhtamar, one of the rare Armenian churches that still stands erect in today's Turkey, on the historic Armenian lands. The Byzantines ruled the area for a short time, and then Vaspurakan fell under the dominion of Seljuks. Then Mongols took over the area until the sixteenth century, when Ottoman Turks conquered the historic Armenian lands.

After the devastation that the Mongols had brought about, the conquest of Armenia by the Ottoman Turks was, at first, a blessing.

Despite minimal opportunities for cultural and architectural development, Armenians enjoyed relatively fair treatment in Turkey until the mid-eighteen hundreds. Armenians were loyal citizens of Turkey, but did not convert from Christianity to Islam, did not voluntarily intermarry with Turks, and preserved their language, religion and culture.

Armenians were not admitted to the army, but paid a head tax. Like other nations subjugated by Ottoman Turkey, Armenians were not allowed to bear arms to defend themselves. In court, Armenians were not allowed to testify against Muslims. Despite that, many Armenians were good in finance and business; they occupied high positions and played the role of mediators between the Turkish Government and Europeans. This was an additional factor to arouse the jealousy and mistrust of the Turks and Kurds, and increase mistreatments and persecutions.

In 1876, Sultan Hamid II came to power of the Ottoman Empire. After the Russian Turkish war, at the treaty of San Stefano, Armenians brought out their grievances. As much as the initial treaty of San Stefano was favorable to the Armenian Question, shortly after, at the Treaty of Berlin, the revised version was accepted, disregarding the Armenian Question. Loss of interest of European powers to the Armenian plight gave Sultan Hamid II the green light to implement a bloody solution to the Armenian Question. In 1894–96, Sultan Hamid's armed mobs looted and massacred Armenian communities throughout Turkey. The villages located around Lake Van suffered immensely, but the population of Van, with its prominent leaders and newly formed political parties, managed to escape the evil plan of Sultan Hamid II. The massacres had driven law-abiding Armenians into organizing political parties and taking arms in defense. The three political parties: the Dashnaktutun, the Armenakan (founded in Van in 1885) and the Hnchakian were active in Van in the early twentieth century. Revolutionary societies were especially strong in Van because of the progressive character of the people of Van and nearness to the Russian border.

In 1908, Sultan Hamid II was overthrown and the Young Turk Government came to power. Instead of the promised democratization of the country and equal rights for all citizens, the Young Turk Revolution gave birth to a new wave of nationalism. The main goal of the new government was to create a "modern nation state" based on one people and one religion. The new leaders dreamed of expanding the empire to reach the Turkik tribes of Central Asia to create the Great Turan. Christian Armenians were a major obstacle along their way to reach the goal.

At the end of nineteenth and beginning of the twentieth Century, about two million Armenians lived in Turkey, and more than 130,000 Armenians lived in the province of Van. The city of Van consisted of the old walled City with the Urartian Citadel atop of the Great Rock, and the Garden district-Aygestan, where the majority of population was Armenian. The relationship of the City and Aygestan was similar to the East End and West End of London. People lived in Aygestan but had their businesses in the City. Despite the general poverty in Ottoman Turkey, Van was a quite-Westernized city. Nearly all the merchants, bankers, doctors, lawyers, tailors, shoemakers, carpenters were Armenian. In 1914, there were 11 Armenian Schools in Van, and 70% of the Armenian population was literate. There were many libraries, theatres, bookstores and two regular weekly newspapers. Van was a thriving city, culturally and politically. British, Russian, Italian and Persian consulates, as well as American, French and German missionaries, had their premises in Aygestan. Dr. Clarence Ussher, who was sent to Van by the American Board of Foreign Missions, lived in Van for about 14 years and with his wife and other missionaries made a tremendous effort to help the needy and those eager for education. The people of Van and the generations of Armenians who had never seen

Van will always remember Dr. Ussher and his colleagues for their unselfish work.

The Kosparian family was one of the typical families living in Van. Just like other Armenian families, the Kosparians were a clan of three generations living under the same roof. Panos Agah was the head of the clan. His wife was Grandma Marina; their older daughter Pailun and her husband Theos had 5 children. Myranoush, the oldest, was 16; Lianoush was 13; Liavart was 10; and the twin boys, Markar and Ohannes, were four years old. Panos Agah's daughter, Araxi, and his sister's son, Markos, were the other members of the Kosparian household. Misho was the servant and Tavi and Tagi were the pet Van cats. With this, starts the story of the Kosparian family described by 13-year-old Lianoush in her diary.

Part One

The Kosparian Family

Tavi and Tagi

OCTOBER 12, 1913

Loud. That's what my little twin brothers are. They are running around screaming at my two precious cats, Tavi and Tagi, banging pots and pans together. They are so annoying and the cats hate them, for good reason. The boys pull the poor cats' tails and scream in their ears. Tagi is so frightened by them that whenever she sees them, she runs and hides underneath my bed, or at least she tries to. The boys, Ohannes and Markar, who are full of brattiness, pull her by her tail. Tavi, instead of running away, comes to me for protection. He jumps into my arms so I can scold Ohannes and Markar. But they run off, trying to find someone else to bother.

Tavi and Tagi are about 8 months old. They are Van cats, just like all the other cats wandering in Van. To me, my kittens are the cutest and smartest of them all. I have had them since they were little kittens. Tavi (short for *Tagavor*–King) is a boy and is very friendly and loving. His right eye is blue and the left eye is green. That is how Van cats are. Tagi (short for *Taguhi*–Queen) is his sister. She is curious and playful. Her one eye is velvety blue and the other one is brown. That is less common for a Van cat. Both cats are a bit skittish and Tavi is slightly bigger than Tagi. They have long, soft, white fur and Tagi also has a brown patch around her left eye.

They eat yogurt and milk mostly, but do not mind a little chicken or lamb. For the last month or two, they have been also hunting for mice and occasionally bring one home. My older sister, Myranoush, can't stand mice and is very worried about stepping on one.

Grandpa Panos gave me this journal to write poems in it. I love writing poems, so my first poem I will dedicate to Tavi and Tagi.

Tavi, Tavi sitting proud
Purring, purring very loud,
One eye blue, one eye green
You are the sweetest Van cat I've seen.
Tagi, Tagi sitting tall,
Chase the mice and catch them all,
One eye blue, one eye brown,
You are the sweetest Van cat in town.

Kittens, Kittens you make me grin,
Anyone's heart
I am sure you could win.
Through your multi-colored eyes
I'm glad you can see
We were made for each other,
You cats and me.

 ## Harrisah and the Kosparian Family
OCTOBER 13, 1913

Tomorrow is my birthday. I am Lianoush Beglarian the II and I am turning 13 years old. I was born on the Day of Harrisah. The Day of Harrisah is famous, for on that day everyone in Van cooks *harrisah*. Harrisah is a mixture of chicken meat, whole-wheat grain and water that is cooked for an awfully long time. It is cooked in huge pots and mixed with wooden spoons until it's turned into a mush. Every year on my birthday, my family cooks pots of harrisah and then gives it to relatives, peasants and the poor. Actually, this is an old tradition and has been going on for many years.

My Grandfather Panos makes sure that the villages where he owns the mills get plenty of harrisah. Grandpa is the head of our family. Kosparian is Grandpa Panos's family name. My Mother was Pailun Kosparian before she married my father, Theos Beglarian. Because Grandpa did not have any sons, when my parents got married, Father moved into Grandpa's home. It is unusual for a Vanetsi man to move into his father-in-law's house. When men move into their wife's home, they are called an "in-house" son-in-law. Grandpa is the head of our family. So, now our house is called Kosparian-Beglarian household, but most of the people of Van, Vanetsis, still call us Kosparians. Sometimes, I think that Father would rather live in a different house where he is the head of the family.

Most of the time, though, it seems he does not mind being called Kosparian. Father's family home caught fire and was destroyed about 18 years ago when Turkish gendarmes burned Haykavank, the area between the City and Aygestan. They were looking for weapons in the Armenian houses. Father's family was not able to build a new home in Aygestan, so they moved to the village of Lezk. Even before his family house was destroyed, he was interested in marrying Mother, but he was too poor and, according to Grandpa, he did not have a "proper education." Grandpa and Grandma did not consider him as a suitable son-in-law.

Mother was supposed to marry a son of a rich Armenian judge. As far as I know, not long before the wedding was supposed to happen, Mother and the family heard some rumors about her fiancée and his lifestyle in *Polis* (that's what we call Constantinople) that made them decide against that wedding. Father recognized that he, once again, had a new chance, and appeared at the Kosparian doorsteps, asking for the hand of Pailun, my mother. Mother, who was very hurt from her broken marriage plans, begged her parents to let her marry my father. She never regretted her marriage, and 18 years later, many of our relatives comment on what a happy and loving couple they are.

My parents see things completely differently from each other. Mother is very practical and earthy, and hardly has any sense of humor. Father, on the other hand, is quite a dreamer. He can be spontaneous and funny. Even though they are completely different, they fit each other perfectly. I think I am more like my father, otherwise how could I write poetry?

Father is also a very disciplined person who works very hard. Every morning he is the first one to wake up, even before Mother, Grandma, or Misho. He feeds his horse and checks on the animals and the vineyard. Father has an old horse that is named Sipan, after the mountain Sipan, on the other side of Lake Van.

Sipan is a dark brown Arabian who has one white sock. Father is fond of his horse, or more precisely, he adores it. He cares for Sipan like a baby, washes him, brushes him, feeds him and always makes sure that his horse has enough water to drink. Sipan eats a lot of apples; that is his favorite fruit. Also, I think he understands Armenian, or why would my father talk to him all the time? Sipan is an old horse and used to be Grandpa's horse but Grandpa is too heavy now for Sipan, and also, Grandpa prefers donkeys or carriages for traveling.

After breakfast, Father gets up on his horse and rides it to the nearby villages where Grandpa owns seven mills. Father is in charge of the proper running of these mills and at least once every week he visits each mill.

Grandpa is retired, but still likes to keep an eye on the business. Several times a month, Grandpa takes Misho with him and checks on the mills himself. He likes chatting with the villagers, and stays for lunch when he is asked. But even when he is not asked to share a meal, he invites himself. "Hey boy, bring me some of your last year's wine. I still have the taste of it in my mouth from the last time I had it here. You make good wine, boy." Myself, I love the food in the villages. For some unknown reason it is always exceptionally tasty, tastier than the food at home.

At home, Father never contradicts Grandpa, not because he thinks that Grandpa is always right, but because it is useless to contradict Grandpa. As soon as anybody says anything that does not fit Grandpa's ideas, he calls them "sick," and then pretends that he is deaf. At home, Grandpa behaves like a sultan. "Bring this! Bring that!" "Can't you do it faster?" "This is uncooked, I am not a horse!" "This *gata* (a sweet pastry) is salty!" "This is not sweet enough!" "Why is this tea so cold?" Everyone in the family runs around him, particularly women. Grandma frequently shouts, "For God's sake, Panos," but she always does (or pretends she does) what Grandpa asks.

Father is different. He is not like a Vanetsi Armenian man. He is very self-sufficient, able to make coffee, tea, or even breakfast for himself and anyone else.

Sandkhtian School

OCTOBER 15, 1913

Today, school felt like it wasn't ever going to end. Math was even more tedious because I stayed up late last night. I was very tired and yawning the whole time, barely keeping my eyes open. So, the math teacher got the idea that I had mastered "the art of long division." He told me to demonstrate 674 divided by three. I had no clue whatsoever how to do the problem. Slowly, I tackled the fiendish equation. I am proud of myself for actually figuring it out.

Sandkhtian Girls' School is where my two sisters, Myranoush and Liavart, and I go every day. Today, the superintendent announced that for the New Year he purchased a piano and it is on its way from Polis. Now, all the girls 12 years and older will take piano lessons. More lessons are bad, but learning piano sounds interesting. Like Father says, everything is good and bad. Nothing is only good or only bad. I wonder about that.

Misho, our manservant, did not come to escort us home today, so I walked home with my sisters, Myranoush and Liavart. Liavart, who is ten, usually chatters uncontrollably the whole time. Myranoush is sixteen years old and is almost always lost in her field of thoughts.

The three of us like autumn in Aygestan, the Garden District of the city, more than any other season. Almost all the fruits are already harvested, except for the few pears that are too high on the trees to be picked. Trees have been losing the last of their leaves. The ground is covered with an array of different shapes and colors: red, orange, yellow, brown and a hint of green. The foliage reminds me of a multicolor *kilim*, an oriental rug.

We walked by the British Consulate, which is my favorite building in the whole of Aygestan. The consulate is on Khach Polan, not far from the Khach Polan Square, the center of Aygestan. Paved with cobblestone, Khach Polan is the largest street in Aygestan. Two rows of poplars and fruit trees stretch on both sides of the street. All the important buildings, like British, Russian and Persian Consulates, are standing along the Khach Polan. The British Consulate has two large verandas overlooking Khach Street, and lovely flowers in clay pots make their home there. Not far from the British Consulate, we turn right and take Nalband towards the Norashen quarter where our house is located. Norashen is one of the Armenian quarters in Aygestan. Urpat Creek flows along Aygestan, but this time of year, it flows so quietly that it is almost unnoticeable.

The few times when Misho does not come to walk us home, we take the longer way. We passed by the bookstore called "A Letter." This is the only bookstore in Aygestan, but there are two others in the City. A copper pen decorates the door of the bookstore. We look at the books in the window displays. Once a month, Mr. Zaven, the bookstore owner, gets new books. If anything is about romance, Myranoush talks Mother into buying it for her. She has read *War and Peace* in French ten times. To me, adventure books are more fun. I also like *Les Miserables* by Victor Hugo. Cosette is good, but I like Jean Valjean better. He fights injustice in his own way and I admire him for that.

Usually, it takes us 15 minutes to get from school to

home when Misho is with us. He keeps hurrying us, but today we are on our own. Liavart and I climb trees, trying to find any hidden pears on the trees unnoticed by harvesters. We look through the windows of the shops. Myranoush does not care much.

When we finally get home, Tavi and Tagi are usually the first ones to greet us. They look happy to see us. Ohannes and Markar follow the cats. Grandma Marina, wearing her everyday apron, ends the procession. Every day she tells us to wash up, change clothes and come down for the afternoon snack: yogurt, cheese and lavash. I like sitting around the stove, which is nice and warm, now that the days are getting colder. Sometimes I help Grandma or Mother with the dinner, but today we are eating the leftover Harrisah, so I went to my room and worked on my new hobby, writing in my journal.

All leaves turn yellow, falling on the ground
Combined with magic colors, they form an illusive rug.
I wish the wind would never come and blow the ornament away
I wish the winter never comes and freeze it all away.

 ## Misho
OCTOBER 19, 1913

Misho has been with the family for as long as I can remember. He helps everyone and will not refuse any job. Everyone needs Misho. He helps Mother to cook and clean, and Grandmother to prepare food for winter and store it in the *maran*, our basement. He accompanies Grandpa when he's inspecting his mills and helps Father with the vineyard and the barn.

Misho is a short husky man in his forties and he has never been married. He is Kurdish. He knows the Kurdish language, but almost never uses it. He also speaks perfect Armenian and some Turkish. He has never gone to school, and does not know how to properly read and write, though he masterfully reads the names of shops in the City. Sometimes he asks me to help him read and write. In return, I ask him to teach me some Kurdish words.

Misho's father was a shepherd who took Grandpa Panos's sheep up to the green pastures in the mountain for the summer. Misho's mother died while delivering her sixth child. Misho was eight years old and the oldest child. When his father came down from the mountains, he asked Grandpa Panos to take care of Misho until he was remarried, and would then come back for his son.

Whatever happened to Misho's father, he never came back. Misho became a permanent member of the Kosparian family. He was always very attached to Grandpa, and Grandpa could never go far without Misho, either.

We were told a story that one time coming back from the city of Bitlis, Grandpa's carriage was attacked by a band of Kurdish robbers who were famous for mobbing and looting the Armenian travelers. Misho bravely stepped in and talked with the bandits. Grandfather's carriage was left alone and they returned home safely. That day Misho was declared a hero. Since then, Grandpa took Misho everywhere on his long trips. Grandpa is very attached to Misho and loves him like a son, even though Misho is his servant.

Seems like Misho is also the one who almost always finds Grandpa's beads. Grandpa is inseparable from his worry beads. It is a chain of beads that he rolls from one end to another all day long. When he is worried or angry, his fingers move quickly pushing the beads around. If he misplaces his beads, which does not happen very often, the life of the family won't get normal until one of us finds Grandpa's beads.

Autumn Harvest
OCTOBER 22, 1913

September and October are busy months for preparing for winter. Everyone is scuttling around like little ants. The Kosparians, and all the other Vanetsis for that matter, are working hard to fill up their marans. Our maran is a small basement underneath the house that you enter by stairs at the far side of our living room. A door in the wooden floor comes out, pulled by a handle. There is the big food cupboard that you can walk into. It is always cool there.

There, in the depths of maran, the family stores the food for the winter. Neatly stacked next to each other are layers of dry lavash, our bread, covered with a white cotton cloth. According to Grandma, lavash needs air to breathe. White cheese is stored in some wooden barrels, and in other barrels are numerous balls of dried yogurt that magically turn into soup when you add water. In clay jars, there is cooked lamb meat, swimming in fat. Pieces of it are scraped and made into wintertime dinners. Dried vegetables like eggplant, okra and beans are in cloth bags and are used to make winter soups and tasty dishes. Dried fruits (my favorite)—apples, figs, dates, peaches, apricots, and raisins—are hanging from the ceiling in cloth bags and will embellish the New Year's tables. In the far corner of the maran we store tarekh, dried and salted fish that is caught in Lake Van. Rows of *basturma*, slices of beef covered with red spices, hang from the ceiling like fish on a line. Every time you enter the maran, the pungent smell of the basturma hits you in the nose. Even when the basturma is all consumed, which happens shortly after New Year, the smell never goes away.

Far in the corner, Mother keeps her stash for the "Black Day." Black Day food is stored in a wooden trunk and is never touched until next summer. I could never fully understand the concept of the Black Day, but from a vague explanation given to us by Grandma, it is the day when we would not be able get out of the house and find food. The thought of a day like that scares me and seems quite unrealistic, so I don't think about that at all. All it means for us is that we can't touch that stash of food.

Mother cannot stand any disorder in the maran. Everything is arranged neatly. The boys and the cats are not allowed in to this sacred food palace. Mother likes to have full control over the maran, and not only the maran, but also everything and everybody's life. She rarely changes her mind. When it's about the maran, I am in full support, but with other things, not always.

It takes days and weeks to fill up the maran. It's a busy time when lavash for the winter has to be baked. After wheat is harvested, it's taken to Grandpa's mills where it is crushed between the millstones into flour. Most of the flour Father sells to the bakeries and shops. Some of the flour is brought from Grandpa's mills in big bags to our house. Then the women turn it into dough. Grandma refuses to hire help to mix the dough for lavash. She says that other women don't know the secret ingredient in the dough. I have been trying and trying to get her to teach me this recipe, but she won't. I think she should teach me this ingredient so I can pass it on to my children and their children so this secret forever remains in our lavash. Bah! I bet there isn't a secret ingredient in her out-of-this-world lavash.

Once the dough is made, Father Tiran blesses it. Then Grandma hires women to do the rest. The bakers roll the dough into thin patties, then stretch those on the stretching boards and slap it to the hot walls of the *tonir*, the clay pit used for baking lavash. When the first batch of lavash is coming out of the tonir, everyone is swarming around the bakers. Imagine the best thing you've ever tasted. This is twice better. Lavash is crunchy, warm and melts in your mouth within seconds. For a whole day, lavash is baked from dawn to sunset. Once it cools down, Mother and Misho take it to the maran and neatly pile it under the cloth.

 ## Grandma Marina's Stories
OCTOBER 25, 1913

Days are getting shorter and colder. Grandma Marina says that it will be raining tomorrow. She knows it because her joints are hurting. It may sound silly but her predictions are usually accurate, so I trust her aching joints.

Grandma says all kinds of strange things. For example, if you do not finish your food, your spouse will be ugly. Chewing gum at night is like chewing on the meat of a dead person. If you do not brush your hair before going to bed, you will have bad dreams. Sneezing an odd number of times is a good sign, and if you sneeze an even number of times, it's bad news. So if you sneeze an even number of times, you must come up with another sneeze. Then it is a sign of wealth. If your skin turns yellow, then looking at a fish in a pond will restore your skin back to its natural color. Yeah, right. And many other things like that.

Interpreting dreams is another of Grandma's favorite topics. She usually interprets those for Myranoush, who has more dreams than the rest of us. If you put on shoes in your dream, you will travel. Having a little baby in your dream, you will hear some big news. Raw meat and fish are bad news and so on and so forth. Myranoush is seeing little babies and shoes a lot. I wonder why?

In the morning when Grandma wakes us up for school, she loves to repeat things. She yells, "For God's sake, get up, get up, get up!" then changes to, "You are late, you are late, you're late!" Five minutes later, she repeats it all again and shortly after that announces, "Wake up for God's love, it's dinner time already." Hurriedly we rush downstairs, wiping our eyes with cold water until we realize that we have plenty of time before school starts.

Grandma Marina is very religious, prays a lot, and cannot stand it if anybody forgets to pray or misuses God's name. Most of her sentences start with, "For God's sake, or for God's love." She also worships her late father, my great grandfather Haj Agah. Haj Agah was given his name after he went on pilgrimage to Jerusalem. Thus, she considers her father the only true Christian in the family and praises him all the time.

In contrast, Grandma does not like to talk about her mother, Mariam Khatoun. Khatoun is an endearing term for an older woman. Everyone used to call her Mariam Pasha for her legendary brave behavior. Mariam Pasha was known to ride astride a horse. She rode fast, not like the other Vanetsi women, who only used horses without carriages during their weddings to take them to the church. Pasha is usually an honorary name given to men when they committed some important bravery. My great grandmother got her name for her love of horses and riding them like a man. There are also some stories about her that no one knows if they are true.

Those days, women could not go to the market and bargain or shop. When her husband was gone for almost a year on his pilgrimage, Mariam Pasha came up with a very brave trick. She put on her husband's clothes, wrapped her head into man's headpiece and, as a man, went to the market. At the market, she changed her voice and talked like a man. By most Vanetsi standards, it was considered obscene, but I am proud of my great grandmother. Grandma does not like to talk about her mother, but sometimes her sister, Katik Khatoun, tells us some stories about Mariam Pasha.

 ### Markos
OCTOBER 29, 1913

Markos is my mother's cousin. His mother was also Grandpa Panos's youngest sister. Their family used to live in the

Karoian quarter of Aygestan. Petros, Markos's father, had a business in Polis and was spending most of his time there. When Markos was 15, his mother died. Petros came to the funeral and went back to Polis a week or two later. He asked Grandpa Panos to keep an eye on his 15-year-old son until he graduated from the Boys' College. A year later, Petros came back, announced that he was getting married, sold his house in Van and took Markos with him back to Polis. Markos was very attached to Van. He was participating in new young Armenian groups and always wanted to come back to Van. For three years he studied chemistry in Polis, and after that he returned to Van, where he began teaching chemistry at the Eramian School. Because he did not have a house or a family of his own, Grandpa offered him to stay with us until he got married.

There was another reason why Markos did not want to leave Van. According to Grandma, he was the only son and was very attached to his mother. His mother's death was a horrible blow for the boy and he could not recover from it for many years. The first several years after his mother's death he was spending long hours at the cemetery. He was frequently disappearing from home and even from school. First, no one knew were he was, but then they found out that he was going to the cemetery to visit his mother's grave. He never accepted his stepmother and became estranged from his father. Despite his father's insistence, he did not to go back to Polis.

I don't remember his mother, but Grandma says Markos looks very much like her, with the same light brown curly hair, wide forehead and powerful chin.

Markos loves butterflies. While in Polis, he studied zoology as a part of his education. He thinks Vaspurakan has the most beautiful variety of butterflies, different from the ones found in the coastal areas of Turkey. He has a huge collection of butterflies and moths. The happiest day for him is when he finds a butterfly that is not in his collection.

LATER

Island of Akhtamar

Markos's favorite places to chase and collect butterflies are on the island of Akhtamar and the foot of the Varag Mountains. Butterflies love plants and use them for food and for laying eggs. I think they also like to rest on the old stones and churches, and there are plenty of places for them on the island. When the doors of the churches are open, in a beam of light, you can see dozens of butterflies fly into the church. It looks as if the light invites the butterflies for a dance. Some fly in, others fly out. Butterflies like sun and light. Once they are in the church, the darkness repels them out. But butter-flies have a short memory. Once they are out, they rush in again. I love watching this game over and over. Wild flowers, mint, tarragon, oregano, and lavender greet and attract these beautiful creatures, which make the scenery colorful and cap-ture your attention for hours. Thousands of tiny, colored scales form their wings. They also have a head with eyes, a pair of antennae, a chest and a belly. My least favorite part during the hunt is when he sticks a needle into the butterfly's chest. From a cheerful insect, the butterfly turns into a frozen statue, like jewelry that no one can wear.

One time I confronted him. "Markos, but you are killing them," to which he replied, "Now they are going to be around forever and no enemy can swallow or chew on them." The poor butterflies have lots of enemies: spiders, birds, frogs, lizards and many others. I feel sorry for them.

Markos is very careful when he is catching butterflies. The wings are very fragile and if you are not gentle, you will break the wings and lose the color. Once Markos catches them, he examines the insects with a magnifying glass. There are hundreds of butterflies that are described in his zoology books. Then he finds the name for it. Butterflies belong to the family of Lepidoptera (Markos told me that). That is butter-flies' last name. Then he finds its first name. He hopes to find a butterfly that is not described in the book. Then he will be a discoverer of a new butterfly.

Markos frequently takes Araxi, Myranoush and me for a butterfly hunt with him. He does it on one condition: we should not try to help him with catching the butterflies. We girls are picking flowers and making beautiful flower crowns while he is occupied with his hobby. Myranoush is not inter-ested in butterflies at all. She always picks daisies, and pulling the petals recites, "love me, love me not." That is her hobby. Araxi sometimes plays the ritual, but I have never heard what she says.

When Markos goes to Akhtamar, the largest island on Lake Van, he almost always takes us with him. We call the lake Vanalich, and love going to it. It is the most beautiful lake you have ever seen—all the Vanetsis say so. Its waters change color from light blue to dark blue. The breeze makes small waves on the water that hit the shore and quickly go back into the lake.

The legend says that Vishap, a dragon, lives in Lake Van. The breeze is the dragon breathing, and when the dragon gets bigger, the breeze turns into a storm. According to the legend, an ancient Armenian god, Vahagn, plunges into the lake and drags Vishap into the sun. Vishap then burns into ashes and falls back into the lake, where it again turns into a dragon. Strong winds are called *Vishap kami*—dragon winds. Grandma liked to tell the story of the Vishap, but Ohannes got so scared that Vishap's name is now forbidden in our house.

In the summer, the boys from nearby villages swim in the lake. Women from nearby villages wash clothes in it. Fishermen, on fishing boats, are fishing for tarekh, the only fish that inhabits Vanalich. The waters are so salty and hard that it is surprising any fish survives in it. The Tarekh survive because they live in the areas were fresh water river falls into Lake Van, so the water is not as bitter. The lake never freezes, even though it gets very cold in the winter. Also, because of the salt, swimming is much easier. When I was a child, I used to swim in Vanalich all the time. But now, I am a grown-up girl and I am not supposed to go swimming, though frequently I have a temptation to jump in the water and swim right to the island of Akhtamar. Instead, we take a small boat to the island.

Akhtamar gets its name from a sad legend. A beautiful girl named Tamar lived on the island. She was in love with a young man from a village nearby the island. Every night she was waiting for her lover, holding a lantern in her hand while he swam to her.

Many other men in the village were also interested in Tamar and wanted to marry her. So, one stormy night, envious of the young man whom she loved, they extinguished the lantern. The young man could not find his way and drowned in the tempestuous waves, moaning, "Akh . . . Tamar!" Tamar was unable to tolerate the pain and died in sorrow. The words from the young man's lips can still be heard in the dark, and the island was named Akhtamar.

On the island is the beautiful Church of the Holy Cross, where a group of monks live. King Gagik I founded a town and this gorgeous church was erected in the center of it. The town was destroyed, but the Church of the Holy Cross, built from pink sandstone, has stood proudly through the centuries. King Gagik I had his own image carved on the façade of the Church, showing him presenting the model of the Church to Jesus Christ.

There are many other sculptures around the church, also. My favorite is the sculpture of Madonna with a child. Even though she is carved out of stone, she seems to have a stare penetrating through centuries and touching your soul. When I look at her I always want to ask, "Are you talking to me?" Other carved images are of kings, princes, priests and herdsmen, and also Adam and Eve. Images of wild animals like wolves, wild cats, snakes, bulls, camels, deer, bears, and mythical creatures like eagles with ram's heads, fishes with dog heads, and stone wreaths of grapes and pomegranates adorn the busy walls of this fascinating church. Many themes were on the mind of King Gagik and his architect, Manuel, who built this church. Every time I go there, I find a new sculpture.

There are many churches in Vaspurakan, the broad area including the city of Van and the area nearby Lake Van. Vaspurakan means "land of princes," and was also the name of the Armenian Kingdom ruled by King Gagik I. Van and Vaspurakan have changed hands between Persia, Turkey and Russia several times. Even though Armenians changed rulers, they kept their language, faith and traditions and continued to build churches. Churches mean a lot to Armenians—they build churches even before building their own homes. Some Armenian churches are very big, like the Holy Cross, on the island of Akhtamar, while others are smaller, like the ones in Aygestan and the villages. According to Grandpa, the size of the church reflects how strong the Armenian king or the ruler was when that church was built. King Gagik I was a very powerful ruler, and it was during his reign that the beautiful Church of the Holy Cross and many other churches were built.

The days when Markos takes us with him for butterfly hunting, the nature and the history always inspire me.

One day water was with water, with nothing in between,
So God put in an expanse of sky, and the mighty waves were seen.

Yippee! Hurrah! The waters seem to say, I can roll crash, foam, be free
I'm soaring like an eagle, hey just look at me!

The waters above were just as glad, rain could finally come on down,
The clouds way up were smiling bright, and seen was not a frown.

Markos likes butterflies, Myranoush likes flowers and I like the Lake Van.

 ## Older Sister
NOVEMBER 1, 1913

Myranoush, my older sister, is very lucky! She is graduating from school in seven months! There are two things that happen to girls in Van after they finish the school. Either they get married as soon as they get their graduation certificate or they don't get married. The latter happens when no suitable candidate is set up for the marriage. This is not the case with Myranoush; she is engaged to marry the lawyer Garabedian's son, Senik.

Myranoush is graceful, pretty and always pleasing. When she dances Armenian folk dances, she looks like a swan. As a matter of fact, even when she talks or walks, she is so gracious that it seems that she is dancing. Everyone loves Myranoush. Grandma says that Myranoush is so pretty that she should tell the moon, "Don't come out tonight, I will shine for you instead." At school she gets only five and plus, the highest marks. It is kind of unfair and hard for Liavart and me to be her sisters because everyone expects us to be like Myranoush. I do not like that. Sometimes I wish she had some flaws. Actually, I think I am more assertive than she is. You have to be assertive to be heard when you live in a large family like ours. Myranoush can be ambivalent and undecided about certain important things and, in my opinion, it does not serve her any good.

Many young men would like to marry Myranoush, but Mother and Father agreed upon Senik Garabedian, who is named after the King Senikerim, one of the kings of Van many centuries ago. Senik's family is wealthy and is well known in Aygestan. He is 24 years old, near-sighted and wears a pince-nez when he wants to see something up close. He has a small forehead, brown eyes, sharp nose, thin curved moustache and no real smile. He seems always nervous around Myranoush, but otherwise looks overly self-confident. He rarely laughs. I think it's because he's afraid of the pince-nez falling off his nose. When he does laugh, it reminds me of the cough of an ill person. He is studying in Polis to become a lawyer like his father. The remarkable thing about him, besides what I've already mentioned, is the perfect Turkish he speaks. Most of the Armenians of Van don't speak Turkish that well. His mother says that he is very gentle and will take good care of Myranoush. Having said all that, I have a major suspicion that Myranoush does not care about Senik at all, but she is not strong enough to break the engagement.

Hagop Avanian from Bitlis is her hero. Myranoush met Hagop in Artamet, where his family owns a house, not far from our cottage. Every summer when we spent a couple of weeks in Artamet, they spent a lot of time together. Hagop looks like a country boy with broad shoulders, open forehead, light brown hair and deep blue eyes.

Last year in August when Hagop's family invited us for a dinner, I caught Myranoush and Hagop kissing behind the curtains. I was shocked, but also intrigued. Being engaged to Senik, Myranoush was kissing Hagop! Myranoush does have a flaw, after all! I decided not to tell Mother what I saw, but asked Myranoush about it and even blackmailed her a tiny bit. She turned beet red and begged me not to tell anybody. After that, occasionally she would share her thoughts with me about Hagop. She calls me her secret adviser. At night before going to bed, we undo our long braids and brush the knots off. During this daily ritual, we tell secrets and dream about our future. Actually, most of the time we are trying to sort out Myranoush's complicated love life.

Hagop's family moved to America. His aunt had moved there after the 1896 massacres, and, in September, she sent them tickets and their whole family left Bitlis for America. They sold their house in Bitlis, put a big lock on the house in

Artamet, and sailed to the new life. Hagop, who is 22 and is very much in love with Myranoush, promised her that he would come back to Van, marry her, and take her back to America with him as soon as he is settled.

Meanwhile, Mrs. Garabedian is pinching Myranoush's cheeks at every chance she has, hoping that she will bear beautiful, rosy-cheeked grandchildren. I am not particularly fond of Senik anyway. Moreover, I dislike his mother. One time, she pinched my cheek so hard I was on the verge of tears. Then she asked mother, "Why is Lianoush's skin so dark? Does she have a disease?"

Last week, Senik was visiting from Polis and came to talk to Myranoush. She pretended that she was ill and refused to see him. To me, she actually looked ill, even though that day she was perfectly fine at school. She looked more relieved later, after her conversation with Mother.

Later in the evening, she told me the topic of her conversation with Mother. Myranoush asked Mother for permission to break her engagement with Senik. Mother listened carefully to her as she talked about her love for Hagop. Mother thinks that the lawyer's son, Senik, is still a better choice for Myranoush; besides, they live in Van. They diplomatically reached a final decision that satisfies both of them. Mother is not sure if Hagop will be back or not. Myranoush, on the other hand, is sure that nothing can stop Hagop from returning from America, so they agreed to leave things as they are, wait for news from Hagop, and not say anything to Senik. After all, he is going to Polis tomorrow and will be back in nine months after he finishes school.

Meanwhile, Myranoush's favorite place in Van is the telegraph post. That is the closest place to America.

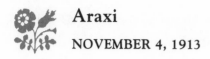

Araxi

NOVEMBER 4, 1913

If Myranoush's romantic life is tangled, Araxi's is complicated in another way. She is mother's younger sister, 24 years old and not married. Everyone is sure that she never will marry. A 24-year-old woman who is not married is considered an old maid. Grandma Marina is not as pessimistic. She hopes that one day some man will lose his wife and will ask Araxi to marry him. Sometimes, I think that Grandma would not mind someone losing his wife just to have Araxi become a mother to his children and, hopefully, have her own children as well.

A normal path for a Vanetsi girl is to go through expected events. First, she has to be a "good girl," which most of the time means "keep her dresses clean." Then, she has to get good marks at school, while at home mastering the art of "making good *sarma*, (rice and spices wrapped in grape leaves), and gata," "learn how to fluff the wool from the blankets," and so on. Then, the Vanetsi girl gets married, and she should be a humble daughter-in-law. At that stage, Vanetsi women are not even supposed to talk. Once children are born, raising children adds to the rest of the work women do. All this, until finally, the woman becomes a mother-in-law and gets to command and talk as much as she wants. Of course, the last job of the Vanetsi woman is being a sweet grandma who tells a lot of stories and has time to pray a lot. Grandma gets to choose and does what she likes to do.

Araxi has left the familiar path. She is spending most of her time at the American Hospital run by American missionaries. She studies nursing and is determined to become a nurse. At home Araxi is very quiet. Sometimes I feel like she is hiding a secret behind her motionless, peaceful soft smile. She talks very rarely, only when she needs to answer a question. Her face is covered with multiple craters left after she had smallpox. Two other children in the family died at the time. I do not know why Araxi is not married. Was that because of her pockmarked face or something else? Despite the craters on her face, I still think she is quite beautiful.

 ## American Missionaries
NOVEMBER 29, 1913

At the end of the Norashen quarter of Aygestan, American missionaries built their compound. Dr. Ussher came to Van from far-away America, and has been living in Van for many years. He and his wife, Mrs. Elizabeth, opened schools, took over orphanages and built a 3-story high American Hospital on their premises. They also opened a mixed girl-boy school in the City.

Americans look different from Vanetsis. Their skin is lighter; their noses are different. Vanetsis definitely have bigger noses than Americans, Germans, Russians or Italians. The foreigners are also dressed differently. Men never wear fez hats and their trousers are cut differently: not as loose at the "seating area" and not as tight below the knees. Women wear pretty dresses and hats like the ones from French books. Dr.

Ussher, one of the first Americans who came to Van, is a famous doctor. People say that he can do miracles and cure people from deadly diseases. Mrs. Ussher works mainly with little children, many of whom are orphans. They also run a preschool which Ohannes and Markar attend twice a week.

To the admiration of Vanetsis, the Americans speak fluent Armenian. Sometimes their Armenian sounds funny, but it is far better than our English. I know girls who go to American School and they have told me that everyone who goes to the American school has his own Bible. The Bible is not the only thing they are teaching to the Armenian children and adults; they also teach arts and crafts, and even nursing. Araxi went to study nursing, and after she got certified, stayed there as a nurse-helper. She brought home a Bible in English. We had a Bible at home in Armenian. We are learning the Bible stories at school and I always score five and plus on the tests, but it is hard to read it in old Armenian. The little English that we know helps us to read the Bible in English. Unfortunately, English or Armenian, all the Bibles in Turkey have one similarity—the word Armenia is cut out of every single Bible. Turkey does not allow the word Armenia in the Bible.

Everybody in Van, Armenians and Turks respects the missionaries. After all, they left their homes and came to Turkey to help people. The American Hospital is the best in Van. Americans are treating Armenians, Turks and Kurds, everyone who needs help. Sometimes I wonder what makes these foreign people leave their homes and families and go to far away places, even if that far away place is our Van.

Van in This Life, Paradise in The Next

DECEMBER 11, 1913

The days are getting shorter. Soon it will be New Year. Van is now all white. It is quieter in the winter because you cannot hear the birds and the crickets. They leave Van for some warmer places and come back in spring. Varag Mountains and Sipan Mountain are covered with white caps now. Mountains surround Van, Varag in the East, Sipan in the North and Nemrut Dag in the Northwest. There is another mountain called Ararat that is the biggest mountain on the Armenian Plateau, but we cannot see it from Van. I saw Mount Ararat once on the way to Bayazet when Markos took us there on a butterfly hunt. Ararat is the tallest mountain and is always covered with snow, even in the summer.

Grandpa says that we are blessed to live in the most beautiful part of the world. I don't know how he knows about it, because he has not been to many places himself. Grandpa's (and a lot of Vanetsis') favorite phrase is "Van in this life, Paradise in the next."

I believe them, though, because that is what the Painter, Panos Terlemezian, says too, and he really has been everywhere in the world. I have watched the Painter drawing frequently near Lake Van. Once, I saw him painting on the Island of Ktuts. In the summer, it is windy on the island, so he was wearing a large gray jacket and a black cap protecting him from the wind and the sun. He was facing the lake and the mountain, Sipan. Twirling the paintbrush in his hand, he was creating magic. The blank canvas was turning into a colorful landscape as the swipes of his brush turned paint into flowers, meadows, water and mountains. While his brush was resting on the easel, he was looking at the waves of the Vanalich, trying to get acquainted with each wave and follow its path as it disappeared on the shore. Then, he would pick the rested brush and make some of the waves darker. Sometimes, I think that his paintings are so perfect that they are better than nature itself.

The Painter has been to Germany, France, Moscow, St. Petersburg and Tiflis to show his art. The Vanetsis are very proud of him and respect him immensely. The Painter confirms that Van is one of the most beautiful places in the world with its Lake Van, the mountains, Urartian fortresses, Armenian churches and palaces. The Painter can settle any place in the world, but he always comes back to Van

 ## The City of Van
DECEMBER 18, 1913

We are beginning preparations for the New Year celebration, which will be very festive. Food is taken very seriously by Vanetsis, and they compete for the variety and amount of food displayed on the New Year's table. If someone's table is not loaded with food, then that person is worthless and disgraced. "Shameless" is how the woman of the house is described when something like basturma, for instance, is missing from the table.

Most of the shopping will be done by Grandpa, Father and Misho, usually a week before the New Year. First though, Grandpa goes to the Market in the City, to check out the produce, or, actually, the prices on the food. Yesterday, he took Misho and me with him. Normally they would've gone without me, but yesterday I was Grandpa's hero. I found his worry beads, which had been lost since early morning. In return, he offered to take me to the City.

Our carriage passed through the Tabriz gate and we appeared in the old city of Van. The City is surrounded with a medieval wall and gates serve as entrances. Oh, I love going to the City! The Market is noisy and busy, and my favorite parts are the Armenian Churches and Mosques from centuries ago. Those are scattered within the walls and the four gates.

Many conquerors passed through Van and left their mark on the City. The most famous one was the Assyrian queen, Shamiram. She was a great queen and built castles and bridges, aqueducts and gardens all over the City. Shamiram has built so much on this land that sometimes people call the City "Shamiramakert," meaning the city of Shamiram.

In Van, behind every name and building there is a story. Shamiram had a lot of power and wealth. She had thousands of vassals and subjects, but she fell in love with the Armenian King Ara. Ara was famous for his looks, and his nickname was Ara the Handsome. Ara refused to marry Shamiram, for he would not betray his Armenian Queen. In response, Shamiram declared war on Armenians, and in a fierce battle between the Assyrians and Armenians, Ara was killed. Shamiram sent her mythical animals to lick Ara's dead body and bring him back to life. The magic did not work, but Shamiram stayed on this land in her sorrow and turned the place into a prosperous City. It is a legend, and I have heard it many times and like to hear it again.

Topchu plaza is the center of the City. There are all kinds of shops, restaurants, libraries and bookstores around it. The American high school is five minutes' walk from the Plaza.

There are seven Armenian Churches in the City. The Armenian churches were built a long time ago and they all look kind of alike, but they are very different. My Mother was baptized at the church named St. Nishan, and so was Grandpa Panos. St. Poghos and St. Petros are two churches right next to the Topchu Plaza and both are always crowded. At five o'clock, the church bells ring from everywhere, but when you are at the Market, the bells from St. Poghos and St. Petros are the loudest. When the bells ring in unison, I feel lightheaded. In the winter, usually the five o'clock bells mean that it is time to close the shops. There are also three beautiful mosques—Ulu Jami, Hosrovi Jami, and the Kaya Chelebi Jami—which are very colorful and make the City look like a place from fairy tales told by Grandma.

The famous Rock of Van stands at the north end of the City. If you stand on the Rock, the city looks so small you could fit it in the palm of your hand. It is a breathtaking view. The City rises from the bottom of the Rock and spreads into the valley towards the east.

The Rock of Van has seen a lot of history. Long before the Armenian kingdoms, and even before Assyrian queen, Shamiram, the Kingdom of Urartu was prospering on this land. The Urartians built fortresses, temples, gardens and bridges. This was more than two thousand years ago, and Urartians were building their fortresses on top of huge rocks and mountains. As difficult as it was, they had to do it to protect themselves from enemies. One of the fortresses, built on

top of the Rock of Van, is called the Citadel of Van. On surrounding stones, Urartians left numerous writings. We do not
know much about Urartians because we cannot read what
they wrote, but the foreign scientists have been working for
many years trying to find clues to their writings. All we know
is that their kings chose the area of Van, built their capital
there and called it Tushpa.

The name of their kingdom was Biainili which gave rise
to the Armenian name Van. Earthquakes and wars destroyed
most of Urartian fortresses and temples, but there are still
many Urartian edifices in Van reminding us about the mighty
Kingdom of Urartu. Urartu was a powerful kingdom that one
day disappeared forever, leaving behind only monuments and
inscriptions. Many wars and earthquakes happened on this
land, but the fortress of Van was indestructible. I hope that
the Rock and the ancient Urartian fortress, with its secret
power, are always here standing guard to protect the City from
enemies.

When we come to the City, Grandpa always visits his
friend Levon Agah at his shop where he sells kilims brought
from Polis, Persia, Tiflis and Kharabagh. He has several shopkeepers, so he does only the bookkeeping. Grandpa says his
job is counting the money.

When we visit his shop, Levon Agah orders some coffee
for himself and Grandpa. They are classmates and like to sit
in restaurants, talking about the changes that happened since
they left school. Today I am with Grandpa, so they cannot go
to the restaurant. Sometimes, I wish I were a man so I could
go to a restaurant, too.

Frequently, Levon Agah visits Grandpa at our house, so
I know him quite well. He is funny and likes to tell jokes

about Vanetsis. I think he makes up some of those jokes himself.

While Grandpa and his friend were talking, I walked outside the store. Even in the winter there are many Van cats wandering around the shops hoping for a piece of chicken or at least some yogurt or milk. Most of the cats have a home where they are fed, but they still love the hospitality of the shopkeepers.

After we were done visiting with Levon Agah, Grandpa checked out the prices of the meats and sweets brought from abroad. Our maran does not have this type of food and it is very expensive. The Market is very busy, as it is the beginning of the New Year's rush. Armenian, Turkish, and Kurdish merchants were praising their produce. Grandpa stopped at a shop that was selling tobacco and coffee. He usually bargains with the seller for 5 minutes and never buys anything if the seller does not come down on the price. After he bought coffee he said (as he always does), "Last year that robber was selling coffee for a lot cheaper." Always the same phrase!

By the time we came home, I was exhausted. I had a bowl of yogurt soup and went to bed earlier than usual. It was a clear winter night and I could see the bright stars in the sky.

The stars tumble into the sky,
Like clowns cartwheeling on the circus stage,
And when morning comes, they twinkle and bow
Exiting the sky, they shine goodbye.

Part Two

The Start of The New Year

New Year and Family

JANUARY 2, 1914

Van is all white. The poplars in Aygestan are covered with snow. The houses, too, are covered with snow and all have smoke coming out of the roofs that makes them look very much alike. It is New Year. Right around New Year, the schools are off for three weeks and restart only after the Armenian Christmas (Epiphany). Even before the actual New Year, our house is in a holiday mood, and the kitchen is filled with food and sweets. It gets dark early and is very cold outside, so we spend most of the time next to the warm stove drinking rose petal tea, eating gata and discussing the passing year. Mother says we eat gata faster than she can make it and starts to hide it from us, saving it for the guests.

Grandma is knitting socks for the twins. Her fingers are crooked from arthritis, but move very fast, magically turning the five knitting needles in the midst of the yarn. The socks she makes are usually very warm, but for some strange reason, they are usually smaller than the feet they are made for. Once she is done and we try the socks, she claims regretfully, "Your feet have grown in the last week." But we have found a new solution. If the socks are made for me, they fit Liavart; if they are made for Myranoush, they fit me. In any case, someone gets a new pair of socks. If the socks for the twins come out small, we will give them to some little kids in the villages. Actually, it is very cold outside and the socks really do come in handy.

Later in the evening, when it is dark and hard to read with the light of a lantern, we beg Grandma to tell us stories. She tells us stories that her Grandmother told her, but I think she makes some of them up. Her stories include dragons, demons, cannibal girls and snakes turning into handsome princes, and they always have a happy ending. When she gets tired while we are still begging her to tell us another story, she says, "Fine, I'll tell you one more story. Once upon a time, once upon a time, once upon a time, there was a big, black, hissing cat." Then she stops.

"Then what, Grandma?" everyone asks, even though we all have heard this story many times.

Then she repeats with her crescendo voice, "Once upon a time, once upon a time, once upon a time, once upon a time, there was a big, black, hissing cat." And the same thing over and over again, except every time she adds another, "Once upon a time." That means it is time for us to go to bed.

On the actual New Year, Vanetsis visit each other all day long. They taste the food and talk about food, how soft, perfect or too salty or not-greasy-enough it is. Roasted lamb, pilaf with lamb, dolma with meat, dolma with beans, lentils and rice, gata, baklava and dried fruits embellish the tables of Van. My favorite is *aghandz*, roasted wheat mixed with hemp seed and salt, a treat that we get only for the New Year. It is crunchy and salty, and it is hard to stop eating it. Grandma says no one can make aghandz like hers. She might be right again.

My cousins, Agassi, Serpouhi, Alice and Iris came with their family. They also live in the Norashen quarter of Van. After they visit us, later on we visit them. Agassi is the oldest son of Tikin Tagouhi (my mother's cousin) and Gevond Agah. He is an extraordinary student and even though he goes to the Central School of Van, the fame of his brilliance is spread all over the City and Aygestan. When parents are unhappy with their children, they ask, "Why can't you be like Agassi?" They don't even need to mention his last name because everyone knows that it is Agassi Khanjian, the older son of Gevond Agah.

Agassi has jet-black hair like a hay stack on his head. His black, clever, observant eyes sitting on both sides of his aquiline Armenian nose make him different from everyone else. I have noticed that Agassi has grown a lot and is participating more in adult male conversations. He listens attentively, changing his sight from one speaker to another. He has been always reading a lot, sometimes even books that are forbidden in Turkey and brochures and flyers that were brought from Europe. He is becoming more unrestrained in his expressions, talking about people named Marx and Engels and their ideas that he wants us to understand and follow. He used to play with us, but now he is obsessed with the ideas of "liberty" and "independence" for whatever it is. Only a year ago he was playing hide and seek, but suddenly he started to feel superior to us, which irritates me immensely. Having said that, I should admit that Agassi is known for helping anyone who needs any kind of help.

But the three girls are great playing partners. Time passes too fast when Khanjians are visiting us. When it is very cold outside we ask Katik Khatoun, who is Grandma Marina's sister and Agassi's grandmother to tell us about Mariam Pasha, who is all the grandchildren's favorite.

I like the cold snow outside and the warm houses of our relatives in Aygestan where we get hugged, kissed, and served delicious sweets. The New Year is a time for new adventures. It is a time for hopes, and we Vanetsis hope for another peaceful year in our beautiful homeland of Van.

In another four days we will celebrate Christmas, the birth of Jesus Christ. There will be more food and sweets, but Christmas is usually celebrated only with immediate family. No more guests. On the night before Christmas, we will go to the church, Saint Astvatzatzin of Norashen, and listen to the Divine Liturgy. We will see most of our relatives there.

American missionaries celebrate their Christmas about a week before New Year. Even though we have the same Jesus, we celebrate his birth two weeks later. Every year, Americans prepare a little play about how Jesus was born in the manger. They invite some Armenian children to attend. I think my cousin, Vartan, can conduct a play like that. I shall suggest it to him.

Grandpa's Pal

JANUARY 21, 1914

In Van, neighbors can visit you without an invitation and stay for supper. It does not happen with many people, but Grandpa's friend Levon Agah does it all the time. First, he will stay for dinner, always praising Grandma's and Mother's cooking. Then he will stay for coffee, tea and talk, talk, talk. Grandpa and Levon Agah both were students of Khrimian Hairig and thought that Khrimian Hairig was the messiah for the Armenians.

Khrimian Hairig has been dead for some years, but he was someone frequently mentioned in the arguments between the older generation, Grandpa and Levon Agah, and the younger generation, Father and Markos. Grandpa has Khrimian Hairig's picture on his wall. It was cut out from an old newspaper and is nailed to the wall. The picture has faded from light and years, but you can still see his dark, sad eyes and a huge, hairy gray, beard.

Khrimian Hairig was born in Aygestan, to a poor family. He lost his father at an early age and was raised by his uncle. He had an incredible thirst for learning and was self-educated. He became a teacher at the girls' school in Polis and became very famous for his teaching and preaching of love for Armenia, its nature, traditions, and culture. He was the first among famous Armenians who praised simple people. He traveled all over Armenia, talked to people, learned from them and taught them how to see the beauty of their country around themselves.

Years later, he came back to Van as a priest and started to print the first Armenian newspaper in Van, which he called *Artsvi Vaspurakan*, meaning *Eagle of Vaspurakan*. Like an eagle flying over Vaspurakan, his newspaper was spreading news around. Through his newspaper he started to circulate stories and letters to Armenians about Armenia. Khrimian Hairig also opened many schools, including some of the first schools for girls. He started a printing shop at the Monastery of Varag and opened a school for boys there.

As a representative of Armenians, he went with an Armenian delegation to Berlin, trying to inform the big countries like France, Britain, Germany and Russia about the suffering of Armenians in Turkey. But, he found that the foreign countries had more important things to discuss than the lives of some Armenians in Turkey. In his own words, Khrimian Hairig "dipped his ladle into the big pot of harrisah called a

Liberty Stew that was served to the countries, but his ladle was made out of paper when others' were made from iron. His paper ladle got soggy and fell into the harrisah." What Khrimian Hairig meant is that he tried very hard to bring the attention of big countries to the "Armenian Question," but was not successful. The "Armenian Question" was about the inhuman conditions, poverty and injustice that Armenians suffered in the provinces of Turkey.

"Where guns talk and sabers shine, what significance do appeals and petitions have?" These were Khrimian Hairig's words when he returned to Armenia. His voice was not heard, then he "cried," but his cry was not heard either. Still, he was Grandpa's idol. After all, he did so much for Vanetsis.

Father and Markos, on the other hand, support the political parties and are hoping with these new revolutionary ideas to help Vanetsis find their independence. Both Father and Markos are participating in meetings among the party members. Frequently, I hear Markos claiming that "paper ladles and pens are useless; we need arms and ammunition."

In reply, Grandpa snaps, "Your parties are going to bring trouble on us."

Mother says that the arguments between men were about the difference in opinion of young and old. She remembers that when she was a child, her father, my grandpa, and her grandfather, Haj Agah argued because her grandfather thought that Khrimian Hairig's ideas about opening schools and learning about the Armenian heritage were heresy. Now Khrimian Hairig's ideas were considered conservative by Father's generation. Father, who never contradicts Grandpa, was getting too excited and ready to lose his temper. "We have to be prepared, we are a small nation and can be swallowed by big nations unless we have sharp teeth ourselves." I am assuming that by sharp teeth he means weapons. Now it was Grandpa's time to surrender. He was not used to seeing Father with foam at his mouth!

"Pailun, bring some more rose tea and tobacco," Grandpa yells. The debates between two generations are quite loud, but the men always part as friends. Levon Agah always has something funny to say. Today, before he left, he looked at my father and said:

Respect the old,
We are wise and bald.

 ## Turndez
FEBRUARY 14, 1914

Yesterday was Turndez. It is a tradition that has been celebrated through centuries. It is a celebration for all the girls and women who are engaged or have been married for less than a year. First, people go to the church and come out with lit candles and start a big fire with a blessed light. Once the fire does not look dangerous, all eligible girls and women jump over it. The rest of us, girls and boys, stand in a long line taking turns to jump over the fire. It is still winter so the fire fades quickly and all of us run back and forth trying to jump as many times as we can. This is really Myranoush's Turndez, but no matter what everybody told her, she refused to jump.

"For God's sake, Myranoush, go, jump over the fire that will burn all the evil so only success and happiness will come to your home," said Grandma, at least three times. Once I heard it, I got an idea. I got close to Myranoush and whispered in her ear, "It does not mean you should marry Senik, it could be Hagop." Myranoush looked perplexed, but shortly after my hint she turned to me. "Come on, Lianoush, jump with me." She grabbed my hand and we ran towards the fire and jumped over it together. We held each other with one hand, with the other hand we kept our dresses raised. I feel like the two of us can do everything as long as we are together. After we jumped over the fire, Myranoush looked relieved. Feeling that she had accomplished her Turndez duty, Myranoush wanted to go back home. It was cold outside, and we came inside where Mother was getting ready for the party: Myranoush's Turndez party. Liavart stayed outside and continued jumping over the fire. I felt torn between my older sister's complicated love-life and my own interests. I would've preferred to stay outside and keep jumping until the fire turned into a heap of ashes.

Araxi avoids noisy events like that. I also feel pity for her. She is now 25 and is not engaged or married, so Turndez is not for her. Every girl in Van wants to have a Turndez for herself. I think that is not fair; it should've been a holiday for all girls and women.

"How was your Turndez?" she asked Myranoush, without showing a lot of interest. Before Myranoush could even answer, she continued, "Walking home I noticed that there are more fires than usual. I guess we will have a lot of weddings in Aygestan this year," continued Araxi, wiping the dust off the wineglasses in preparation for the party.

Myranoush just shrugged her shoulders. It was obvious that she would like to be done with the party as soon as possible. I wanted to jump in and tell them how much fun it was, but realized that none of them were interested.

Then Araxi started to tell us about what Mrs. Ussher told her. In America, they don't have Turndez, but they have another tradition that is celebrated in February and is called Saint Valentine's Day. Men send pretty cards to women, with some poetry or words on the cards. Elizabeth Ussher showed Araxi the card that she had received from her husband. It said, "You are my Valentine and I fondly, truly love thee." Myranoush was mesmerized. "That is the most beautiful thing I have ever heard," she moaned.

After all the fires were quenched, there were parties in the houses for brides and newly-wedded women and, according to the tradition, the brides are also given presents. Mrs. Garabedian sent a present to Myranoush, an apron and a tablecloth. Myranoush did not even want to unfold the presents and look at them. Mother said that the tablecloth was brought from Polis and is most likely worth a fortune. It is hard to believe that a tablecloth can be worth a fortune, but even if it had been pure gold, Myranoush was not excited about it.

I think Turndez is fun. And every time it's finished, I wait for the next one to come. The fire challenges you for adventure, and I dream about my own Turndez.

The Crane by The Name Pandukht

MARCH 18, 1914

The roses are blooming in our garden and also all over Aygestan.

The air is full of sweet scents, the rose smells best of all,
It stands out from all the rest, with petals that slowly fall.

They come in many colors, yellow, red, white and pink,
Yellow like a summer sun, white like a little mink.

Red, like a hot, steaming fire with a scorching flame,
Pink like a child's rosy cheeks, playing a wonderful game.

The reason this place is called Aygestan is because this part of Van where we live is a big garden. Every house is surrounded with poplars, fruit trees, a vineyard and a rose garden. Vanetsis eat the fruit and enjoy the scenery from June to October. People of Aygestan have put fences surrounding their property, but neighbors visit each other from the side gates opening into each other's gardens. For us kids, it is a great way to play with other kids. I think I overheard one time that the purpose of the gates was a route to escape from your home if you can't use the front door.

In the spring it rains a lot, but it hardly ever rains in the summer. It has been raining so much that Urpat Creek is flowing cheerfully through Aygestan, filled to its banks.

Poplars are everywhere in Aygestan and the City. Every spring a crane family returns to a nest on the old poplar tree next to our house. The cranes stand on one foot and watch the world go by. Every year I am worried that the cranes will not come back. To my surprise they always do. We named our favorite crane Pandukht. Just like humans, the cranes wander to far away places to the south and come back home. Grandpa says that Armenians of Van are like cranes. Many leave Van for whatever reason, like studying, work, or marriage, but then they return.

Armenians have lived in Van for many centuries. Grandpa, his grandfather and his grandfather's grandfather all lived in Van, so Grandpa says that we are the real Vanetsis. Our roots go back two thousand years. Grandpa built the house that we live in, and before that, his family lived in the house where our barn is now. People lived in one-story houses with a tonir at the center of the house with a big hole in the ceiling for the smoke to get out. In the winter when it was very cold, they even brought the cattle into the house! That made the house smelly, but cozy. The old houses did not have any windows, and were made out of mud. People still live that way in the villages. Grandpa hires people to keep the barn clean, because our tonir is still there.

Van is in Turkey, or in the so-called Ottoman Empire. Armenians lived on this land for more than two thousand years, long before the Turks came. Osman was one of the first Turkish rulers who started to expand his land; his followers were called Ottomans. Ottomans were warlike and predatory and conquered the land of many non-Muslim countries including Armenia and formed the Ottoman Empire. The Turks conquered Vaspurakan in the early 16th century and have been ruling it since then.

Armenians and Turks live together on this land. Our church and we Armenians are of a Christian faith called Gregorian. The name of the church comes from the name of

Gregory the Illuminator who brought Christianity to Armenians in 301 AD. Gregory had been taken hostage to Byzantine as a young boy and was raised there. He converted to Christianity and returned to Armenia to preach the new religion.

Later on, Gregory came to the Armenian King Tirdat, preaching Christianity. In the beginning, King Tirdat persecuted him for not worshipping the ancient gods and imprisoned him for many years in a deep well with spiders and tarantulas. Years later, King Tirdat got sick and was told that only Gregory could cure his strange illness. So, the king released Gregory and was, indeed, cured. In response to that, the king converted himself and thousands of Armenians into Christianity. Thus, Armenia was the first country that accepted Christianity as the state religion.

Our savior is Jesus Christ and we read the Bible and pray in churches. The head of our church is the Catholicos and now it is Catholicos Gevorg V. Surenian, who is the 127th Catholicos, counting from Gregory the Illuminator. That is how old our church is.

Turks are of Muslim faith. They read the Koran, which is their holy book and pray in mosques to God, whom they call Allah.

We go to Armenian schools; Turkish children go to Turkish schools. They look like us, we look like them, but we do not talk much to each other in Aygestan, even though most of the Armenians can speak Turkish and Turks understand Armenian. In the villages, Turks wear robes, Armenians wear loose pants and shirts; but in Van, both Armenian and Turkish men wear trousers and coats and fez hats.

Armenians are keen on education, and many go to

Europe to study. The wealthiest people in Van are the Armenian merchants. Turks have the highest positions in the government. All of the gendarmes are Turkish. Armenians and Turks are cautious of each other and they don't mix very often. The animosity between Turks and Armenians is centuries old, since Armenia was conquered by Turks. It heated up after Sultan Hamid II, the former ruler of Turkey, in 1895-1896 ordered the slaughter of thousands of Armenians in many provinces of Turkey. At home, we are told that Turks are our enemies, they conquered our land and want to have our land without us. When Armenian children play on the streets, the bad guys are always Turks and the good ones are Armenians.

The City is different. In the market, every shopkeeper speaks both languages, whatever helps to sell their goods. Some Armenian families in the City have Turkish friends, their neighbors. My second cousin, Hermine, and her family live in the City. She has a friend, Zeina, who is Turkish. Zeina is a sparkling girl with blue eyes and short cut hair, right below her chin, but most of the girls in Van, including me, have long braids.

Zeina's father is the principal of one of the Turkish schools in the City. Zeina was born in Paris, where her father was studying. They use a lot of French words, like *mon ami, cheri, merci* and other words. Her Van cat (Zeina says *chat*) is named *Chocolat*. I think chocolate is a dark brown, sweet candy, but Zeina thought it an appropriate name for her cat because her cat is so sweet, even though all the Van cats are white. Oh, well. Zeina is an only child and is very spoiled and rather shallow, but I like her because she is funny and carefree.

Once, when Hermine and I visited Zeina at her house, Zeina took us to the Turkish room. Some Armenian houses have Turkish rooms, too. As a rule, children are not allowed in the Turkish room, which is a large room with a beautiful large rug on the floor and several smaller rugs covering the corners. Colorful *mindars*, round oriental pillows, and other pillows are spread all over the room, so guests can be pampered and comfortably seated on the floor. The room is exclusively for adults, for smoking and drinking coffee. Once we got to the room, Zeina started a pillow fight until feathers were flying about the room. In excitement, we did not notice how the beautifully arranged room was transformed into complete disarray. We ran back to my aunt's house hoping we will never be confronted about the mess we made. Thankfully, they never did say anything to my parents.

Zeina's father is a nice man. One time I heard him saying a toast at my aunt's house. He was saying that Armenians are builders, creators, historians, and artists and for Turkey to prosper it needs the talent of its Armenian population. When we came home, Father said that Zeina's father is an honest man, but most of the Turks, particularly ones in the Government, do not think the way he thinks.

Vartan's Play and Celebration of The Armenian Alphabet

MARCH 20, 1914

All eleven Armenian schools of Van are celebrating the 1500th anniversary of the creation of Armenian Alphabet. The celebration is going to be at the Varag Monastery. Saint

Mesrop Mashtots is the person who invented the Armenian Alphabet. Actually, he was a preacher and a scholar who was teaching Christian faith in the early fifth century. Armenians had a spoken language for hundreds of years before Mashtots, but they were writing mostly in Greek and Persian. The traditions and the history were passed on through generations in stories told by parents to their children, and children to their children, and so on. We needed a written language, Armenian letters. Mesrop Mashtots spoke many languages, like Greek, Persian and Syrian. He spent years trying to create a written language for his people. Just like the spoken language was different from other languages, Mesrop Mashtots created a unique alphabet that perfectly reflected the spoken language. 36 letters (later 2 more letters were added) that we are still using today were first used to translate the Bible, and then used by different historians to record the Armenian history. Once the letters were invented, people could write stories, letters and poetry. It is hard to imagine that some time ago there were no Armenian letters. We are grateful to Mesrop Mashtots (now I can write my poetry and my journal) and this year we are celebrating 1500 years of the discovery of our letters.[*]

Our school is preparing very hard for this celebration. My cousin, Siranoush, is the star among the students. She will be saying a prayer of Saint Grikor Narekatsi, also known as Narek. Saint Grikor Narekatsi was a tenth century Armenian preacher, and was the author of The Book of Prayer. Siranoush and I are in the same class, and we learned about Narek in our class.

---

[*] The Armenian Alphabet was created around 404-405 AD, but there is evidence that the 1500th Anniversary was celebrated in Van around 1913-1914.

Always neatly dressed, Siranoush looks like a miniature copy of her mother, Tikin Tigranouhi, who is my father's sister. Despite her age, which is the same as mine, she seems like she had been a grown-up once and now is here to bring the wisdom to children like me. Almost always, she manages to beat the expectations of the teachers. Her Armenian is always perfect, sometimes even better than the Armenian teacher's. She can speak eloquently even about a cup of milk.

Siranoush's two older brothers are both in Germany studying at the University of Leipzig. She is very proud of them and is planning to study there, too. She adores her brothers, but is dissatisfied with her younger sister, Varsen. Varsen is a real tomboy. She always manages to get grass stains on her white dress. Aygestan is covered with grass, flowers and trees, and Varsen always gets into trouble. I completely understand Varsen's point of view; unfortunately, my mother does not like Liavart or me to climb trees, either.

Siranoush likes to eat apples with butter. That gourmet dish seems quite ridiculous to me. Apples are fruits, and butter belongs on bread. I can't see it going anywhere else!

My second cousin, Vartan, is directing a play about how Mesrop Mashtots finally came up with Armenian alphabet. Despite his youth, Vartan has an exceptional interest in the theater. He gets his talent from his Uncle Karapet Ajem-Khachoyan, who is the most famous actor in Van. Vanetsis, in general, love theater and it is always a big event when the local theater comes up with a new play or the visiting actors bring a play from Polis. Uncle Karapet plays the leading role in the majority of plays. Vanetsis like to tease him, "Here comes Yago," or "What would you say, Hamlet?" or "Which god are you today, Karapet?" Uncle Karapet himself has plenty of funny stories about the reactions from the audience. My favorite is the story that happened during Shakespeare's Othello. During the play, the audience got very angry with Yago, the character uncle Karapet was playing, and started to throw tomatoes and other objects at him. It has happened before, and those times, he masterfully missed the flying objects. But, one time he was not able to dodge from the tomato flying at him and the tomato smashed right into his cheek. All he could do was to borrow Dezdemona's famous handkerchief to wipe his face.

Vartan never misses a play. He also loves to draw and always carries a pencil and paper with him. Before he conducted our play, he drew just about all the moves we had to do during the play. He himself played the role of Mesrop Mashtots and also a role of an old Greek priest. Vartan has pronounced features with dark curly hair and a classical Vanetsi nose. Even though he is shorter than most of the other kids involved in his plays, he is always very convincing. Gurgen, who is Vartan's cousin, played Sahag, Mashtots's student, who translated the Bible into Armenian. I play another one of Mashtots's students. In theaters in Van, men usually play the roles of women. On the contrary, in Vartan's plays, girls play women; in fact they sometimes play the roles of men. So, I am one of Mashtots's students and I am wearing Grandpa's oriental robe for my part. My part includes only one sentence, "Master, our people love the letters and are grateful to you." When it is time to say it, I make my voice hoarse, trying to sound like a grown-up man. I wish Mariam Pasha, my great grandmother, could see our play. After all, during her times, girls did not even go to school.

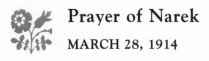

Prayer of Narek

MARCH 28, 1914

The celebration of the Armenian Alphabet was really impressive. Father Eznik blessed the event and spoke about Mesrop Mashtots and his role in the Armenian history. Siranoush said the prayer of Saint Grikor Narekatsi, which is a lot longer than the part I memorized.

> *Before I was, you created me.*
> *Before I could wish, you shaped me.*
> *Before I glimpsed the world's light, you saw me.*
> *Before I emerged, you took pity on me.*
> *Before I called, you heard me.*
> *Before I raised a hand, you looked over me.*
> *Before I asked, you dispensed mercy on me.*
> *Before I uttered a sound, you turned your ear to me.*
> *Before I sighed, you attended to me.*

Thousands of Vanetsis gathered in the yard of Monastery of Varag. It is a perfect place for events like this one. All the missionaries and their families came, too. The celebration of the birth of the Armenian Alphabet was a big success. Our play was a hit.

Varag Monastery complex has seven churches surrounding a rectangle courtyard, but only the main church is functioning now. There is also the printing shop, started by Khrimian Hairig where the first Armenian periodical, *The Eagle of Vaspurakan* was published. It is no longer published, but boys from the Varag Monastery School are still taught the business of printing.

An Armenian, King Senekerim, built the church of Varag. King Senekerim was married to the daughter of King Gagik I, Princess Khoushoush. In the eleventh century when the Byzantines started to attack the Armenian kingdom, in order to rescue his people, King Senekerim left Vaspurakan and ordered his people to follow him to the area called Sebastia, or Sivas, which is northwest of here. He had a vision that by moving away from Vaspurakan he would save his people, but he kept his love for Van in his heart. When Senekerim died, his wish was fulfilled; his body was brought back to Vaspurakan and buried at the Varag Monastery. Right next to him is the grave of the Queen Khoushoush. But, many Vanetsis stayed and settled in the Sebastia region. Grandpa says he can always spot the real Vanetsis from Sebastians, they have the same bump on the noses as the people in Van have.

I'm very glad I don't have any bumps on my nose.

 ## One Sunday Morning
APRIL 5, 1914

It is Sunday today. I woke up from the sunbeam resting on my face and tickling my nose. I am happy to be Vanetsi, I thought. I love all the stories about kings and queens, and wonder if, maybe, I am a great, great granddaughter of one of the Kings of Vaspurakan? I should force Grandpa to exercise his memory.

"What wonderful things could I do today?" I asked myself.

"Lianoush, come downstairs," I heard Grandma yelling. "I want you to learn how to wrap a perfect dolma, to impress your future mother in law." Now that Myranoush has mastered the art of dolma wrapping, Grandma is after me. So much for my royal dreams.

"I will be right there, Grandma Marina," I shouted in response, disguising the annoyance in my voice. "Just let me finish a poem that is on my mind."

> *The bright shining sun*
> *Gives warmth and light*
> *To blooming flowers*
> *On a bright spring morning in Van.*

 ## Easter Eggs
APRIL 12, 1914

Today is Easter. Grandma colored about thirty eggs last night. She used the red onion peel and boiled the eggs in it for a long time. The eggs turn into dark deep red color. Every Easter we have egg fights when everyone picks an egg, then goes up to someone who also has an egg and challenges him or her to an egg fight. You and your opponent take turns tapping the eggs against each other. One of the eggs always cracks. The person whose egg lasts longest without cracking, wins.

Markar and Ohannes started the egg fight long before we went to the church. By the time we came back from the church all the eggs were broken, some smashed. Liavart and I were upset that the boys broke all the eggs. Only one egg survived the battle and that was Markar's "winner" egg.

My cousin Siranoush's family came to celebrate Easter with us. Varsen was very upset because there was nothing to celebrate; the boys already broke all the eggs. Before dinner, Siranoush was asked to say the prayer, the same one she said last week at the celebration of the Armenian Alphabet. I could have said it too, but nobody asked me.

The Easter dinner was as usual, rice pilaf with dried fruits and walnuts. That is my favorite type of pilaf, but Mother makes it only once a year on Easter. Broiled tarekh from Lake Van and spinach are the other components of the Easter dinner. Grandpa said that there was not enough butter in the pilaf and the tarekh was overly broiled and turned into "pieces of dried fruit." There were also beans and lentils with chopped herbs, but Grandpa considers it poor peoples' food and does not even bother criticizing it.

We will finish the school year soon. In the summer, it gets very hot in Aygestan, so we spend most of it at our cottage in Artamet. Artamet is located about 13 kilometers south of Van, and is a place where most of the wealthy Vanetsis have summer homes. Our cottage is very close to Lake Van and the breeze from the lake makes the evenings very pleasant. This year Myranoush is not looking forward to that because Hagop is not going to be in Artamet.

Constantinopole

MAY 29, 1914

Markos had to go back to Polis and visit his father, who has been ill. He stayed in Polis for almost three weeks and returned with a large trunk with all of his belongings and also some sweets for us. I overheard from Grandpa and Mother's conversation that the real reason for his travel was a marriage that his father had planned for him. As a matter of fact, Grandpa was sure that Petros Agah was not sick at all. In any case, Markos came back earlier than we expected. Perhaps he did not like the bride, or like Grandma says, he would never live far from his mother's grave. Myranoush and I wondered if Markos has someone from Van in mind. But who?

Earlier tonight we all had some fancy tea and Turkish delight that Markos brought from Polis. All of us were listening to Markos talking about Polis. I did not realize before how much feeling Markos has for that city. "It is a beautiful city and I love and hate it at the same time. Constantinopole is a home for many nations. When you walk on its steep narrow streets, you see Greeks, Turks, Armenians, Jews, Arabs, and Egyptians, rushing down its alleys to their businesses. These people have no desire to be anybody but themselves. When you are on Galata Bridge which connects Galata and Pera, you hear noises of sirens and steamers and the yelling of Albanian, Corsican and Montenegrin boatmen. Constantinopole is a beautiful city, standing on seven hills and compressed between two seas. It is a mongrel city, both old and modern, bearing culture and history of many nations. There are numerous mosques and many old churches built by Byzantines. Some, like Santa Sophia, were changed into mosques. Another, Saint Irene, was painted ugly pink and now serves as an armory and museum.

I noticed the fascinated smile on Araxi's face, she could not take her eyes of Markos. Actually, I was quite fascinated myself, but why does he hate that city?

"Yildiz Kiosk next to the museum had on sale a set of furniture that belonged to Sultan Hamid. The legs of tables and chairs were made of guns and revolvers. You wonder who was invited to sit on these chairs. . ." I think Markos was asking himself the question.

Markos stopped and said to us, "All of us have school tomorrow and Araxi has to get up early, too." Grandpa, Grandma, Mother and Father, had all gone to bed some time ago. "And you girls. . ." Markos started. . .

But we did not let him finish. "Please tell us some more about Polis," we all pleaded.

"The 'bloody' Sultan was overthrown and exiled, but the Young Turk Government did not bring any good to the people of Ottoman Empire. Armenians and other Christians still have no rights and frequently live in fear. Not only that, thousands of Armenians have been slain in Constantinopole while European countries have silently watched the actions of the new Turkish Government." Markos looked and sounded disturbed and serious.

After a pause, he gave a weak smile and continued, "When I was studying in Polis before, my favorite place was the large paved court of the Pigeon's Mosque, also called Bayazet II, in the old part of the city. There were always lots of pigeons around. One of my Turkish friends was a letter-writer who sat all day long writing letters for people who could not write themselves. He had a little table with bright blue inkstand, a quill pen and a stack of white paper. There were many letter-writers near Pigeon's Mosque then. At certain times I helped my friend, when he had to write too many letters." Markos continued after another short pause. "When I went there this time, there were no letter-writers, the marble fountain was dry, the place that was busy before was now almost empty except for few worshippers, but the pigeons were still everywhere. An old Gypsy in a long colorful robe and an unreadable look was sitting on the pavement. Every now and then, he threw grain toward the birds. Hundreds of pigeons would attack the small grains, and for a moment, the light was dimmed by the swirl of the pigeons, with grains in the beaks, flying up toward the arches and minarets of the mosque. Once the square was empty, the old man would fling more grain. The pigeons have stayed there for food," concluded Markos, and he stopped speaking.

"Markos would you like to move to Polis?" Liavart asked, to everyone's surprise.

"No, I want to live in Van. Van is my home," said Markos without hesitation and with a big smile. "But you girls, one day you should visit that beautiful and mysterious city." And then he quickly added with a smile, "But then come back to Van and marry a nice Armenian Vanetsi man."

We all laughed, except for Myranoush, who did not think that was funny. We finally turned in; Araxi stayed to clean up the dishes and though Markos looked tired, he offered to help her.

Grandma says that some women in Polis put something on their lips called lipstick. She says that it is because they don't have enough color on their lips. I wonder if that is true?

Part Three

Farewell to Myranoush

All The Way From America

JUNE 6, 1914

To everyone's surprise, Hagop Avanian came to town today all the way from America. He is staying with his relatives in the City. I am pretty sure I know the reason for his return. Not a lot of Armenians return home once they get to America.

When we heard that he is in Van, Myranoush started to look like a trapped cat trying to get out. Not long after the news came to our house, Hagop showed up himself. Even though Myranoush knew that he might be coming, she almost fainted as soon as she saw him. I pinched her really hard. The technique worked, she remained standing and threw a grateful glimpse at me.

Hagop looked very different. His childish, country boy look disappeared, he seemed thinner and had dark circles under his eyes. He looked much older than his age. He wore his moustache differently; the edges were cut short and did not curl up his cheek, like in other Vanetsi men. Hagop was also dressed differently, more like the American missionaries.

Upon Father's invitation, he stayed for dinner. Hagop and Myranoush did not say a word to each other. Everyone else was asking Hagop about America. Hagop told us about the long sail to America and how his family is getting settled in a big city named Boston. His family is sending their respect and love to all of us.

Grandpa was asking questions about politics, Father about something called an automobile. According to Father, automobiles are carriages for people and they move without horses or donkeys. Hagop explained that automobiles use oil just like the lanterns. Mother asked if they have Armenian

Schools and Armenian Churches. Hagop was not sure if they do or not, but that there are lots of Christian churches, so Americans believe in God. Grandma asked if there are any Turks in America. Hagop smiled and said that he has not seen one. I jumped in and asked if they have Van cats in America. Hagop did not see any Van cats, but lots of other cats.

Everything about America sounded so wonderful, except for no Van cats. That is a problem! Throughout the evening, Myranoush was incapable of uttering a word. I kept watching her out of the corner of my eye to see if she needs another pinch. She looked pale, but not too bad.

Hagop brought a present for us. It was a box that was playing music on its own. It is called a gramophone. There was a flat plate that Hagop put in the gramophone and it started to play a beautiful song in English. Grandma Marina looked perplexed. I think she sensed some competition. I whispered into her ear, "Grandma, this cannot sing your songs."

After dinner was over, it was time for coffee. Hagop stood up and said that he has something very important to say. I knew he is here not only to tell us about America. My heart started to pound; it was time to pinch Myranoush.

Hagop thanked Mother for the generous dinner then turned his face towards Father and Grandpa, took a deep breath and started:

"Dear Mr. Theos and Panos Agah, I traveled all the way from America because my heart is in Van. Your daughter conquered my heart and I came to ask you for her hand." After a moment of dead silence he continued, "I would like to marry Myranoush, and take her with me to America. I have two tickets to sail back to America and we shall go back in three weeks, with your permission and blessing."

Everyone was expecting that he would say something about Myranoush, but his speech was even shocking for me. What Hagop said was so strange and unrealistic that no one could comprehend it. In three weeks, Myranoush will leave home? I got carried away, forgot to pinch Myranoush, and she fainted after all.

Araxi, who was holding the tray of coffee, dropped it, trying to help revive Myranoush. With a thunderous speech, Hagop brought up havoc in the family. After Myranoush was picked up and put on a chair, Hagop got close to her and held her hand. Even though they had not seen each other for almost a year, it was obvious that Myranoush was fully approving his offer. Mother had probably kept Father informed, because he looked less shocked than Grandpa did.

Misho cleaned up the pile of glass and coffee. Everyone was waiting for Father or Grandpa to say something.

"For better or worse, Van is our homeland," spoke Grandpa after a long awkward silence. "This is where my father, grandfather and his father were born, learned to walk and talk, read and write, had families, raised children, built homes and churches and have cemeteries. For centuries, Armenians have lived here. Our land is blessed with every gift of nature. Van is the most beautiful place in the world. Lake Van, Akhtamar, the Varag Mountains, Mount Sipan, the old City and Aygestan are our homeland. God gave us this beautiful land to cherish and not to abandon. What is in that America besides music boxes and self-walking carriages, that my girl should leave the land of her ancestors? I have heard they have those things in Tiflis, too. Why don't you marry her and stay here? We will help you to build a two story house in Hankuysner, not far from here."

Hagop did not look surprised. He expected a reply like that; all the older Vanetsis talk the same way. After all, the saying, "Van in this world, Paradise in the next," is said by Vanetsis, and not only by them. Hagop was not Vanetsi; he was from Bitlis. I am surprised that Grandpa did not bring that up.

Vanetsis like to tease the Armenians from other regions. "Oh those Armenians from Bitlis are completely self-centered and arrogant." "Never give your daughter to an Armenian from Polis, they are obnoxious." "Armenians from Tiflis are empty-headed and speak wrong Armenian, too."

All the other Armenians consider Vanetsis frugal and cheap, plus a lot of other nonsense like that. Knowing Vanetsis first hand, I can attest that Vanetsis are very gener-ous, at least most of the time. I am very proud of Grandpa for not saying anything about Hagop's home city, although I am sure he will bring it up later, after Hagop leaves.

Hagop was looking at Father, waiting to hear something from him, but Father's eyes were stuck to the pomegranate tree outside the window. The tree was loaded with small pomegranate fruit and dark orange flowers like bells hanging over the fruit. We will have lots of pomegranates this fall. Father seemed to be in a different world.

"Panos Agah," started Hagop, "I love my homeland too. It is very hard to leave this most beautiful country in the world and live abroad. But to me, home is a place where my family feels secure. Home is where I am not afraid of being killed or losing my shop every day. Home is a place where sheep are grazing in the meadows and coming home safe and sound. Home is where you can use your talent and education to create, build and bring happiness to people.

"America is not just a country of automobiles and gramophones. It is a country where they don't kill you just because you are Armenian. Sultan Hamid is gone, but Ottoman Turkey rules over our homeland. The Young Turks Government is not going to bring peace to Armenians. Khrimian Hairig could not bring peace to Armenians. English, French and Russians are not going to bring peace to Armenians either. Armenian life is not worth a coin here. Turks have killed us before; they will kill us again. I do not want to raise a family here." He took a sip of water and continued.

"America is a country full of opportunities and dreams. You can go to school, open up a shop, earn money, and nobody will destroy it in one day. Using my knowledge of the printing that I've learnt at the Varag Monastery, I am hoping to open up my own printing shop in Boston. Myranoush will fulfil her dreams, go to school and study nursing."

Myranoush has never told me she wants to be a nurse. I bet she told Hagop about it, because she wants to be like Araxi. Myranoush is too delicate and soft and will definitely faint as soon as she sees blood.

Everybody else was thinking about what Hagop just said. After a short silence, Hagop continued, "It is a long trip, but my family is waiting for us, Myranoush and me. I promise you all that I will care for your daughter just like I would care for my own mother."

Mother started to sob. She felt that for once she is losing control over things, at least her daughter's fate. Father finally turned his head from the window to Myranoush. Her wordless mouth was saying, "Please." It was obvious that her feelings for Hagop were stronger than family ties and her love for Van.

"Enough for today, let's talk about this with clear heads in the morning," said Father and walked Hagop to the door.

Many times I pray for Hagop and Myranoush, even though the thought of not seeing my sister daily seems quite unbearable.

No Van cats in America! I should give Tavi and Tagi some more of Grandma's yogurt.

I wonder if there are pomegranate trees in America?

 ## A Rose Has Blossomed in The City of Van
JUNE 8, 1914

After a long sparring between Grandpa and Mother on one side and the rest of the family on the other, the decision was made to let Myranoush marry Hagop, have a wedding and let them go to America. Araxi helped a lot. Her argument was that Myranoush would be happy with Hagop, and anyone stopping this from happening would have to deal with their own conscience for the rest of his or her life. Araxi was very convincing. I had never seen her more motivated and ambitious. Mother's worries are understandable. Not only would she have to say farewell to her daughter, not knowing whether she will ever see her again, but she also had to deal with Mrs. Garabedian's disappointment of the broken engagement. Broken promises of marriages happen in Van all the time. Mother had her own memories of a broken engagement. More so, she did not want her daughter to be the cause of one.

I really approve of Myranoush's choice and deep in my heart hope that Mrs. Garabedian will never pinch my cheeks again.

The gramophone was playing all day. The songs were about love and more love. To my surprise, the songs sounded quite cheerful. Grandma sings beautifully, but her songs are always sad. All the Armenian songs are sad. I could hear Grandma muttering all day.

A rose has blossomed in the city of Van
A pretty woman with long braids so fine.
I want the whole world and the people of Van
To know, that you, my dear lover, are mine.

I was thinking about "love." What is it? I asked Myranoush that question before. She said that she was not quite sure, but had an answer for me. "Love is when you constantly think about someone, having dreams about that person and want to spend your life with him." Then she referred me to her favorite book, *War and Peace*. "If you want to know about love you should read it." I looked at the book and actually started to read it, but my French is not that good and it was way beyond my patience to understand that thick book. Also, there was a lot about war and I don't like reading about people dying.

So, I decided to ask the other women in the family. Grandma's answer was straightforward, but only remotely touching the real question. "Love is when you care for your family more than for anything else. Love is when your house is neat, food is tasty, children are clean and healthy and you praise the Lord every day." When I tried to change Grandma's thoughts from a perfect Vanetsi woman's image to a "love between woman and man," Grandma had an answer for that, too. "Women marry men because their parents decide that they should. Once you are married you get used to your new life. That maybe what love is about." To me, this was more like a question than an answer. I did not dare to ask that question to my Mother, but tried it with Araxi. Araxi looked amused, it was obvious that she did not have a quick answer for me. "Lianoush, I honestly don't know."

 ## The Family Portrait
JUNE 12, 1914

Today all our family went to Mr. Petros's shop to take our photograph, which is a portrait that is not painted, but magically appears on a paper after we look into a dark box and a flash of light comes out. Mother said we need two pictures of the family with Myranoush and Hagop, one for Myranoush to take with her to America, and one for us.

Grandma, Grandpa, the twins, Liavart and I were in the first row and Myranoush, Hagop, my parents and Araxi were in the second row. Markos could not come, and Misho stayed home preparing the house for the wedding. For a whole hour Mr. Petros tried to position everyone and make sure that none of the children would laugh or make faces during the flash. Mr. Petros was quite annoying by changing his mind several times on which way our jaws should be turned and how our arms should be positioned. Finally, both photographs were taken and after Father paid Mr. Petros, all the family in our best clothes walked through Aygestan back to our house. I was wearing the white dress that Mother made for me this year, for Easter. She made it a little bigger than my size, "better bigger than smaller, you can always grow into it," and now I was suffering the consequences. Because it was baggy, this morning Mother quickly stitched it. In a hurry she did not do a good job cause when I moved my arms, the stitches kept coming apart.

For the photograph, Liavart and I had to roll our braids behind our ears and pin them down. Of course, by the time we came home, that "construction" also fell apart. I do not like formal clothes or hairdos and felt great having my braids tangling down to my knees and getting back into my everyday brown dress that was a hand-me-down from Myranoush.

All the way back from the photography shop, Grandpa complained that Mr. Petros over-charged us. "Four golds? Four golds for two pictures? That man is a robber! I have to work days to make that much!" I don't know what was he talking about because Grandpa really has not worked since my father started to work for him. Nobody tried to calm him down, since the efforts would be useless. He continued to grumble all the way home. I noticed a smile on Hagop's face. He did not say anything, but I am sure that he was thinking about Vanetsis being "cheap."

I thought about the photograph. Mother wants Myranoush not to forget us and for us to remember her face. How can we forget each other? After all, we have lots of photographs in our brains. Though with time, the images fade away and also children and older people do not have a good memory. Personally, I agree with Mother, we needed those photographs and it does not matter how much we paid or how annoyed we were with the whole process of taking pictures.

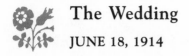

The Wedding

JUNE 18, 1914

Preparation for the wedding created a lot of havoc. A wedding like this is not what Mother and Father had planned for their first-born. They had a very short time to prepare for the wedding. Four lambs were skinned and cooked. Twenty trays of baklava were made. Twenty pitchers of wine were poured and ready to be served.

The wedding took place at Saint Astvatzatzin Church in the Norashen. Father Tiran, who baptized Myranoush 16 years ago, married them.

Myranoush was wearing the same dress that Mother wore at her wedding. It was a long white dress with laces and bands. Her head was covered with a large white scarf, and a veil covered her face. Her forehead was covered with gold medallions that Mother and Grandma wore at their weddings. According to tradition, she was put on a horse, and the procession followed her to the church, where Hagop was waiting for her. The horse was the famous Nazik from the stables of Poghos Agah. Nazik is a beautiful white Arabian horse much younger and tamer than Sipan, and is used at most weddings in Van. The bride's white big scarf with hundreds of beads on it was hanging on both sides of the horse. Myranoush doesn't know how to ride a horse; in fact, she was not even supposed to do anything except to sit on it without falling off. She looked like a statue, I think, because she was scared to death. Father was holding the reins and walking in front of the horse. I thought about our great Grandma Mariam Pasha who was famous for her skillful horse riding and imagined her gracefully trotting without fear. I should ask Father to teach me to ride a horse.

The procession got to the church uneventfully. Father Tiran performed a long ceremony. Ohannes and Markar got very impatient and had to be taken out of the church by Markos. After the ceremony, Myranoush and Hagop together rode to our home, this time in a carriage. Nazik was taken back to the stable, where she will be waiting for the next wedding.

The Garabedians did not show up for the wedding. No surprise. Two weeks ago mother sent Misho to their house with a letter from Father annulling Myranoush's engagement to Senik. Mrs. Garabedian took the letter and did not utter a word. One week ago, after lengthy discussion in the family, Grandpa decided that the Garabedians should be invited. Again, Misho was sent, this time with a letter of invitation to the wedding. Mrs. Garabedian refused to open the door, so poor Misho had to slide it under the door. In any case, there was no trace of them.

A lot of other Vanetsis came to the wedding. It was a celebration of love, family, food, dancing and singing. Young men and women danced the Round Dance together. Men holding hands and moving their feet formed a fortress made of dancers. They looked strong and powerful. Myranoush and Hagop dancing together looked more lonely and vulnerable. They looked like a boy and girl who tore themselves from the strong crowd and are daring to live their own life.

Grandma Marina sang more songs than she knew. I think she had too many cups of *arak*.

Levon Agah was the *tamada*, our toastmaster. He was in

a great mood and was saying toasts and telling many jokes. One of them was about an old Vanetsi woman who visited her son in Paris and then returned back to Van. When she was asked how was Paris, she announced, "Paris is nothing. There are only three beautiful cities in the world: first is Van, then Igdir, and then America." Everybody laughed. That was a new joke that I have not heard before. Vanetsis like to tell jokes about themselves. Excited, Levon Agah told another joke about a Vanetsi who did not want to dump the water after he boiled the egg! "What about the bouillon, I am not dumping the egg broth," he claimed. I have heard this joke many times and so had everyone else, but all of the guests were laughing as if they were hearing it for the first time.

The day before the wedding mother asked Grandpa to refrain from political discussion. All was going well until the men had too much to drink and started to argue about politics. They each took a turn toasting, proclaiming that Van belongs to Vanetsis and nobody else. Mr. Tatikian, who is working for the Turkish Government as an advisor, reminded them that Armenians should be obedient civilians to their government, Ottoman Turkey.

Mr. Suren stood up with a cup of arak in his hand and announced, "For centuries now, we have been enslaved and considered as second class citizens on our own land. When needed, we have learned to bend and not to break, but for how long can this continue? We, the Armenians of Van should raise our heads straight up, drop our chains and look to the North towards our Christian brothers and free future." Most of the guests cheered. Mr. Tatikian immediately got up, thanked Father and Mother and despite my parent's request to stay longer, he left. Arguments and disagreement happen at Armenian parties all the time. Grown-up Vanetsis argue a lot.

Grandpa says that each Vanetsi has a little bit of Bell in himself. Haik and Bell were legendary heroes descending from Noah. Bell was evil and wanted to subjugate Haik. Haik took his clan and went away to a mountainous land. Bell followed him. In a fierce battle, Haik killed Bell and freed himself. The land was called Hayastan—Armenia. All Armenians are descendants of Haik. A little bit of Bell in each Vanetsi usually meant that people of Van sometimes do things that are against their own interests.

The party was still going on, but I was so tired that I had to go to bed. Tavi and Tagi are under my bed, on the floor. They don't like noise. I don't like noise either. Tavi came out from under the bed arched his backed and jumped on my bed. I will always protect my cats.

I hope that, one day, someone like Hagop on a white horse will come after me, too.

 ## Farewell to Myranoush
JUNE 27, 1914

Today, we all went to Avants, the port on Lake Van. Everyone, except for Grandpa Panos. Myranoush kissed his hand and he kissed her on her head and said, "God be with you. Don't forget your homeland, my child. I hope one day you and your family will return to Van."

Mother was planning to send the whole dowry with Myranoush, but Hagop asked her to pack just enough clothes to get to America. Getting to America takes about a month on a big ship. Hagop was planning to buy most of the food in

Polis. We took two carriages and headed to Avants, where a boat with white sails was waiting for them. They are going to cross Lake Van and get to Tatvan, the port not far from Bitlis. From there they will take a carriage to Polis. Everyone was trying to say something to Myranoush. Mother kept telling her "Always wear warm clothes, warm stockings, keep your head and feet warm. Who is going to take care of you if you get sick?"

I was looking at Myranoush and trying to encrypt her image in my brain. I realized that the whole time since Hagop came we never talked about when are we going to see each other again.

"We will see you next year," I said cheerfully. Everybody looked at me as if I knew something that they did not. I knew it was a wishful thinking, but I wanted to say something positive because everyone else behaved as we were saying goodbye to Myranoush forever.

The newlyweds got on the boat. Father's last words were, "Wherever you go, remember who you are."

"I will," answered Myranoush. Her eyes were so red she could not cry any more. She hugged and kissed everyone many times. We watched how the boat with white sails slowly started to disappear in the dark blue waters of Lake Van. Myranoush was standing on the back deck waving. The boat was getting smaller and smaller and finally looked like a pearl sinking into the dark blue waters of Lake Van.

On the way back Grandma kept repeating, "She could shine, instead of the moon." I was getting irritated. First, Myranoush did not die, and second, how about if I shine instead of the moon? Too bad this thought did not cross Grandma's mind.

When we came home, I started to think about the

changes in my life, now that Myranoush is gone to America and I am the oldest girl in the family. The cats can freely come to my room. Mother will probably pass Myranoush's chores on to me. I miss Myranoush already.

I am also very proud of her. She dared to start a new life far from home and family. Maybe that is what love is about?—strength.

Maybe one day I will go to America, too. But who is going to stay in the land of our ancestors?

 ## Vardavar
JULY 24, 1914

Today is Vardavar. Armenians celebrated Vardavar for a long time. It is a holiday praising the pagan goddess, Astghik, who is the ancient Armenian goddess of beauty and water. It celebrates the beginning of the harvest season and the need of water for Armenian peasants. It is an old religious holiday, but for once it is mostly for kids. Girls and boys from Armenian quarters are pouring water on each other. That is the way you celebrate Vardavar. Ohannes and Markar had their share of fun, running around with copper cups in hand—they were totally wet and happy. Those little brats were pouring water on my cats. Tavi and Tagi are not afraid of water, just of little monsters running toward them with cups in their hands.

Mother took us to the Arark Square where the biggest market of Aygestan is located. The market was full of people. Arark Square, the largest in Aygestan is surrounded by the Arark Church, the Arark School and the cemetery. The farmers come from villages with endless heavy carriages pulled by horses and mules. Pears, peaches, watermelons, melons and apples form colorful mountains all over the market. Many farmers had hidden pots of water next to their stands and were pouring water on the kids and customers. It was very hot and pouring cold water on each other felt heavenly. There were also clowns on stilts dancing around with water jugs and sprinkling people from high above. The farmers were shouting, praising their fruit.

"My melons are so big that only two form a whole load for a camel and are sweet enough to make your tongue stick to your palate," one of them was yelling.

"Cold watermelon is what you need this hot day," another one was screaming. Mother picked a watermelon and started to flick on it checking it for ripeness. That is what Grandpa always does.

Suddenly, like out of nowhere Mrs. Garabedian appeared right next to Mother. Until today, Mother successfully avoided her, but now she was trapped.

"Good afternoon, Pailun," she said stiffly. Mother looked like she had swallowed a fish bone, but bravely managed to produce a smile. "Good afternoon, Davartuhi, hope your family is all well. It is a very hot day, no wonder children are enjoying Vardavar so much," said Mother, hoping that it was the end of their conversation. Mrs. Garabedian turned around to leave, but then immediately spun around and hissed, "So, my son wasn't good for your daughter? Humph! You preferred a village boy from Bitlis to my sophisticated, pure-blooded Vanetsi son!" In shock, Mother tried to defend herself. "Davartuhi jan, today's children do not listen to an adult's advice. They want to do things their own way. I am sure Senik will find a wonderful wife."

"Yes, he will. Many girls dream to marry my son. He will be a famous lawyer soon," she said with despise.

"I am praying for him, just like for my own children," said Mother, but Mrs. Garabedian was not interested in what Mother had to say.

"The apple does not fall far from the tree," she retorted, turning around and quickly walking away.

This was exactly what Mother was dreading: to be reminded of her own broken engagement. She was still holding the same watermelon that she was flicking on when we noticed Senik's furious mother. "Let's get that watermelon, I am sure Grandpa would approve it." I tried to distract her from what just happened.

That same very moment, I noticed our cousin, Varsen, with a copper pitcher of water in her hand. Before I could move or say anything, she flung the water all over Mother and me. Any other Vardavar, Mother would just smile, but not today. Soaked and unhappy, Mother shook her index finger at Varsen and yelled, "Lianoush! Liavart! Boys! We are going home immediately!" To the disappointment of the seller, she put the watermelon down, grabbed the boys' hands and we rushed out of the market.

At 6 o'clock, the bells of nearby Armenian churches rang in unison. It was time to stop the watering games and get changed. Too bad we had to come home long before that.

Vardavar is always fun.

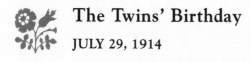

The Twins' Birthday

JULY 29, 1914

Today is the twins' birthday. Ohannes and Markar are turning five years old. Even though the boys are twins, they don't resemble each other at all and also have different personalities. Ohannes has a big head and brown, clever eyes. Mother calls him, "My Bismarck," after the German Chancellor. Ohannes is full of fears and despite Grandma's prayers and rituals, he does not like to go out in the dark or hear scary stories. When both twins have to face something, Ohannes is always hiding behind Markar. Markar, on the contrary, is absolutely fearless. Markar has light hair and green eyes. He is energy-in-motion, and not only physically, but also his brain works very fast. Even at his age, he is very good at math. For that, Mother calls him "My Pythagorus." There is only one thing they have in common: they both like torturing my cats.

It was the first family gathering after Myranoush's wedding. Gevond Agah put the boys on his lap and asked them to recite a poem, but the boys ran away and did not say a thing.

As always, first the dinner was served to men. It was summer dolma: peppers, tomatoes, apples and eggplant stuffed with ground lamb and rice. After the coffee was served, the men moved to the other room and started to talk politics, and, as always, yelled and screamed at each other.

The women and children dined together. The younger children ate in five minutes and ran away. After eating, my three cousins, Liavart and I went to our room, where we mostly talked about Myranoush's wedding, her dress, how pretty she was and how much we miss her. At last, the women were ready for their dinner and gossip. The topic of their conversation was also Myranoush's wedding.

And now, the boys' birthday party is over, all the guests are gone, the boys are peacefully sleeping, and downstairs, adults are having tea, trying to stay cool in this hot night in Van.

I remember the day when the twins were born. I was eight years old at the time. Mother was getting ready to have a baby. Father and Grandpa were hoping to have their first boy. Vanetsi ladies were saying, "Pailun looks very pretty, looks like she is having a boy." Do they mean that when Mother was having a girl, she looked ugly? Anyway, she looked very big and swollen to me.

The Beglarians and Kosparians had three girls and were hoping that the newcomer would be a boy. Actually, there were four girls. Right before I was born, one-year-old Lianoush, the first one, caught scarlet fever and died. Mother was severely distressed, went into labor and I was born the next day after the first Lianoush died. In her memory, they named me Lianoush. That is why Father calls me Lianoush the Second. I like it, because it makes my name sound like a name of a princess.

On this day five years ago, Mother felt that she was in labor. Father brought a midwife. Grandma was also helping. Myranoush and I tried to get into the room, but were thrown out, so we waited in the room downstairs. Grandpa and Father were smoking. Suddenly, Grandma Marina ran out yelling, "It is a boy, we have a boy!" She kept repeating, "Thank you Dear Lord, it is a boy!" Everyone was rejoicing for the first boy in the family and named him Ohannes. Grandma, who went back to check on Mother, suddenly jumped out again, yelling, "There is another boy!" He was named Markar, and even though at birth he came with a small delay, he was always the risk taker, unlike his brother, who was always full of fear.

After the boys were born, Mother, stayed in bed for almost a month. Nana came to live with us and helped take care of the twins. Nana has a story of her own and I should tell it from the beginning.

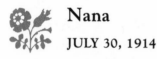

Nana

JULY 30, 1914

Nana was always sad. She had icy blue eyes, brown hair and a dark brown mole under her left eye. Even in the summers, she was wearing a dark headscarf covering her forehead and most of her face. Nana did not know how old she was, but she looked in her twenties. Vanetsi women her age wear a head-scarf only for special occasions: when they go to a church or a funeral. Nana never took her headscarf off. She never went to a church or a funeral.

Nana spent most of her life in the American Orphanage in Van. When the boys were born and Mother was too sick to take care of them, Araxi brought Nana to help us care for the newborn boys. She was supposed to stay with us until Mother got back on her feet, but even after that, Nana stayed with us.

From what Araxi told us, Nana was not the girl's real name. Nana's family lived in the city of Arjesh, which is on the north side of Lake Van. People of Sultan Hamid, the former ruler of Turkey, killed all of her family. Somehow, the little girl escaped the massacre and was hiding for a long time in the orchards and the mountains, until she was found and was taken to the American orphanage. No one knows how long Nana was hiding in the orchards eating fruit and nuts. Some thought that Nana was in the orchards for more than a month, because her clothes were completely ragged and her feet were covered with bleeding ulcers. When she was found, she did not talk or say her name or how old she was. She never said if she remembered anything from her village. She was taught to speak again and given the name Nana because that was the only word the girl murmured when she was found: na-na, na-na. There were many children who lost their parents those horrible days in 1896, but most of them had either a sibling or a memory of who they were. Nana did not. Nana spent 13 years in the orphanage. She learned to read and write and weave rugs. She remained very quiet and did not say a word unless she was asked a question. The three years that she spent with us she hardly talked, and her existence in our house was almost unnoticeable. The boys got very attached to her and I think that the very first word they said was: Na-na.

Two years ago a man by the name Harutun came and found her. He was Nana's older brother. Harutun had been a priest. He studied in a religious seminary in Polis and returned to a village near Arjesh. During the massacre of 1896 in Arjesh, the Turks gathered all the men from the village in the church and shot them. Then they set the church on fire, but Harutun did not die. Once he smelled the smoke, he realized that he was alive, but he was covered with dead bodies. With a struggle, he relieved himself of the bodies and got out of the smoking church. He tried to look for his family, but did not find anyone alive.

Hungry and weak, he reached Russian Armenia, a town called Erevan. Harutun thought that all his family was slaughtered and did not know that his youngest sister had also survived until one day, when he heard about a girl from Arjesh with big blue eyes and a dark brown mole under her left eye. One of the girls from the orphanage had gotten married and moved to Erevan. When she met Harutun and heard that he was from Arjesh, she told him about the girl she knew in Van, who was also from Arjesh. Despite difficulties and the long journey, Harutun came to Van to see the girl he thought could be his sister.

One day he showed up at our doorstep and asked to see Nana. Grandma said that Nana does not like to meet people or go out of the house, but as soon as she heard the story, she ran and got Nana. When Harutun saw her, he said that she looks exactly like his mother. There was no question that Nana was his sister. Her real name was Nargiz and she was six years old in 1896, right before her family was killed. They spent hours together talking to each other, and for the first time, we heard Nana crying. The next day, Nana came to my parents and told them that she is leaving with her brother. She was not wearing a headscarf. Nana was beautiful.

The Gate of Mher

SEPTEMBER 12, 1914

Today at school we were studying the Armenian epic, *Sasna Tsrer*, The Daredevils of Sasun. Sasun is a region in Armenia, west of Lake Van. In the story, Tsovinar, the daughter of King Gagik, drank a handful of milk that spurts from the Rock of Van and gave birth to unequal twins, Sanasar and Bagdasar. The twins were not identical—Sanasar was a big, handsome hero and his twin brother was envious and pitiful. Descendants from Sanasar are three generations of heroes of Sasun: Great Lion Mher, Davit of Sasun and Little Mher.

Great Lion Mher single-handedly killed a lion and scared his enemies for forty years. He died on the same day his son Davit was born. After Lion Mher's death, enemies conquered Sasun. Davit was very strong, but did not know who he was. Once he found out, he got on the Fiery Steed and took his Lightning Sword and defeated the enemies of Sasun.

When Davit's son, Little Mher, was growing up, his father was abroad and when they met, he did not recognize his father. In a fierce fight, Mher killed his father, who had cursed him to be immortal and have no children. Mher was devastated. Guided by a raven, he reached the blind stone portal at Van, and disappeared behind it. Hair grew all over him and he became a wild man. According to the legend, he would come out one day when the stars are right to save or destroy the world.

The epic is very long and has an elevated heroic mood. All of the characters are giants who have good intentions and incredible super human strength, but are surrounded with tragic events. It is a sad story.

According to the legend, Mher is hiding behind the Gate of Mher, which is located on the heights of Toprak Kale north of Aygestan. Not far from it, the Turks built military barracks where they keep ammunition and are constantly surveying Aygestan.

 ## Father's Friends
OCTOBER 1, 1914

Liavart, the boys and I helped Father make wine today. First, we helped him pick the grapes, making sure that all the vines were removed from the grapes. Then he dumped the grapes into a big copper bucket and the boys started to crush the pile of grapes with their bare feet. As soon as the boys got tired, Liavart and I jumped in and started to stomp the leftover grapes. I like the sound of a popping grape when the skin and the pulp get separated. While we were enjoying ourselves in a sea of grapes, Father removed the stems, which he will use to make vinegar for cooking. I had to raise my dress, but still got grape juice all over me. Once all the grapes were crushed, Markos helped father pour the grape mass into a covered barrel.

"To make good wine you should know chemistry," said Markos. Father was happy to get help, even though he does not like to be reminded about Markos being better educated than he is. After all, Vanetsis made wine for centuries without knowing any science.

Once a week, Father and Markos will move the wine from one barrel to another, removing more stems and seeds until the wine is completely clear and the color of garnet. At that point, I can't drink it at all, it is a drink for adults, or like Father calls it, "a drink of Gods." In about a week, the freshly made "young wine" called *majar* is served with dinner. At this time, we are allowed to taste it. After that, it gets too strong and I get dizzy from it. Wine is stored in the furthest corner of the maran for months, and only after that is it ready for drinking.

When Grandma found out that we were making wine, she ran outside and picked a few dozen pomegranates. She wanted Father to make some pomegranate wine, which she uses as medicine and gives to us when we have a stomach pain. She was carrying the pomegranates in her apron, and being in a hurry, she stumbled and let the apron go. The fruit fell on the ground, and the juicy pomegranates cracked open, the dark red juice oozing out making small puddles on the ground. The smashed fruit looked very messy. Grandma looked like a guilty child who did not obey the adults. There was truth to that. Father had told her earlier that he would pick the pomegranates and make her wine tomorrow—but Grandma is known to be impatient. She considers her first thought or desire as a guide for her actions, even when she is told the exact opposite. The juice from the pomegranates quickly stained the ground. Grandma, scolding herself, helped us to pick all the fallen fruit and clean the mess on the ground. Then, we broke the hard skin of the remaining pomegranates and pushed the seeds out of their seats into the bucket. While doing it, we had a feast eating a whole bunch of juicy seeds.

We had a great day today. Father said, "Working with a friend is more fun than work." I felt honored to be called

Father's friend. We all worked hard and as a result, men have their wine, Grandma has her medicine and all of us had lots of fun. Except for Mother. She got more stuff to clean and lots of clothes to wash from grape and pomegranate stains. Mother has the hardest job of all.

The Little Bird
NOVEMBER, 20, 1914

Today I did not go to school because I was sick. I was wretchedly ill and had a splitting headache. Grandma diagnosed me with "sorrow" for not having Myranoush around. Anytime anyone gets sick, Grandma has two explanations as a cause for any illness—it is either the "sorrow" or an "evil eye."

The "evil eye" is considered to be the cause of the disease if the neighbors or some old women recently praised someone too much. Her treatment in that case is lengthy prayer, and the more she yawned when she prayed, the weaker the evil eye became. The other way of destroying the evil eye was putting a blue stone with an eye carved into it beside your bed. We all had the blue stone in our rooms to watch over us. Grandma also has a preventive ritual to take away the evil eye. While someone is saying wonderful things about any of us, she jumps and pinches our bottoms. She says it is easier to prevent the evil eye than to treat it.

"Sorrow" is considered the cause of the sickness if you yearn for something or are sad or distressed about something.

I miss Myranoush a lot. I remember the day on Turndez when we held hands and jumped over the fire together. I feel lonely now. When you see people every day, you do not realize how important they are in your life and find out only when they go away. Something happened to me. I noticed that I have not been able to write any poetry recently. Last month I turned fourteen and suddenly I feet like I have grown up, and not just because people around tell me about it, but really! I feel irritated and annoyed at things that I liked before and can't even ask Myranoush if she has gone through similar emotions when she was my age. I feel the headache again on one side of my head around my right eye.

Mother came to my room and brought me a bowl of Grandma's famous supas, yogurt soup with wheat. I did not want to hear anything from her or maybe I did, but not what she was going to tell me.

"You did not put a jacket on." "Your feet and your hair were wet." "You forgot your hat." "You do not listen to an adult's advice," and so on. According to Mother, all the sicknesses come from catching cold. I wish she would just talk to me, about me or Myranoush or herself. Anything but the stupid "cold."

In any case, I was thankful for the supas. According to Grandma, "This supas will make the sick run and the dead rise." She says it every time she makes supas. I should admit that I felt much better after I had the supas, but still did not want to run.

Soon it will be New Year, but even the closeness of my favorite holiday does not cheer me up. I am fourteen years old now and the oldest child in the family. I miss my sister. We have not had any news from her yet.

Markar and Ohannes are going to the preschool run by the American missionaries, mostly by Mrs. Elizabeth Ussher. They have been learning English, and today when they came home, they started to recite a poem in English.

> *Little bird, little bird, come to me,*
> *I have a clean cage for thee. . .*

I am sure there is more to the poem, but that is all they could remember and they were running after the cats and annoyingly repeating the same verse over and over again. The poem did not make much sense to me, why would a bird be interested in captivity? I rephrased it quickly in my mind.

> *Little bird, little bird, come to me,*
> *I will open the cage and set thee free.*

 ## A Curse for The Family
NOVEMBER 29, 1914

I was on my way to the dinner when I heard Mother's voice from Araxi's room, and was tortured with curiosity when I heard the tone of her voice. This was her unusual voice, the one she uses when she is frustrated and unhappy and does not have the right answer for the problem.

I came close to the door and slowed down. First, I thought that it is about Myranoush, instead I heard, "Araxi, I know that since Tigran died, you think this is your last and only chance. Well, I am sure it is not and there will be many more."

She continued, "Look, Boyadjents Zarouhi married a wonderful man when she was 32. You are only 25. We have always been told that a man and a woman cannot marry unless they are apart seven bellybuttons. He is your first cousin."

"What!" I almost screamed from astonishment, but could not leave my position at the door. Araxi was quiet, while Mother was bringing up all the arguments for why she cannot marry Markos. I remembered the weird energy I sensed several times around Araxi and Markos. They are in love! Who was Tigran? I have to inform Myranoush about my discovery! By seven belly buttons, Mother meant that to marry each other they have to be seven cousins away.

Araxi was walking from one side of the room to another, twisting her hands, and with big tears in her eyes. She still did not say a word. I wonder why is it bad to marry your first cousin? After all, it is just a girl marrying a boy and they have known each other for a long time.

Mother continued, "You are going to bring a curse on the family. You may have disabled children, they will be deaf or mute or blind." I slowly walked away from the door and went down to dinner.

We had my favorite, pilaf with lamb for dinner. Liavart, the boys, and Grandma and Grandpa had already eaten, and Grandpa was sitting next to the window smoking his water pipe. Markos and Father were waiting for Mother to serve the dinner and were discussing the war that Turkey just got into. Father was saying that sooner or later the Turks would start drafting Armenian men. He looked worried. They stopped talking when Mother came down and started to place the pilaf on everyone's plate. When she was passing a plate to

Markos, he asked her cheerfully, "Where is Araxi? Is she at the American Hospital again?" Without looking at Markos, Mother coldly answered, "Araxi is not feeling well, and Misho will take the dinner to her bedroom." I felt a chill running down my spine. I think Markos sensed something and we ate the rest of the dinner in silence.

O, dear merciful God, take pity on Araxi.

 ## A Letter From Boston
JANUARY 29, 1915

Today is a happy day. Mr. Parumian from Arark has returned from America to take his family back with him to America. He is a friend of the Avanian family and brought a letter from Myranoush. This is an exact copy of her letter:

> Dear Mother, Father, Grandpa, Grandma, Lianoush, Liavart, Ohannes, Markar, Araxi and Markos,
>
> I miss you all so much. I wish you were here. Even though the journey to America was very long and hard, we made it safely here. After we had been on the big ship for about thirty days, I thought we would never reach America. Many people got sick and I was not sure that we would pull through. Thanks to everyone's prayers, finally we arrived at a place called Ellis Island. All the immigrants have to go through that place. They questioned us about the reason for our emigration. One official suggested that I change my name to something that is easier to pronounce. The first time Hagop arrived on Ellis Island, he changed his name to

Jacob. The Americans call him Jake. I decided to cut my name down and make it Myra. So, now we are Jacob and Myra Avanian. Actually, they recommended that we change our last name too, but Hagop insisted on keeping his last name Avanian.

When we got to Ellis Island, they kept us in quarantine for two weeks. We were so fatigued and thin after the prolonged voyage that they suspected tuberculosis or some other contagious diseases. We turned out to be healthy and were released to Hagop's family.

Then we took a train and arrived in the small city called Watertown, where Hagop's family is settled. Watertown is smaller than Van, but it is near a big city called Boston. Just like Turkey, America is divided into provinces, but here they are called states, and Boston is the capital of a state called Massachusetts. Boston is much bigger than Van, with tall buildings, many churches, subways, trolleys and cars.

I have seen very many new things here. A trolley is a carriage that is run by electricity and a subway is an underground trolley. Telephones are instruments that send the voice from one place to another, quite far from each other. That means that if I have a telephone here and you have one there we can talk to each other. I hope it happens soon. I'm sure Father would like to see all these moving machines carrying people around.

Hagop and I live in a small apartment. Hagop is working in a printing factory by the paper mill. The company prints newspapers, loads them on carts and then the newspapers are sold to whoever wants to buy them. Hagop learned the trade at the Monastery of Varag, but he had to learn a lot of new things here.

Unlike the Vanetsi women, some American women are working, and so are the majority of the immigrant Armenian women. I will be going to Watertown High School starting next September. Then I will go to nursing school. I was very surprised and impressed to find out that there is also Women's Doctors' School in Boston. My mother-in-law is very nice and supports my wish to study nursing. Or maybe, I will study to become a doctor? But for now, I am learning English. It is a very complex language. When Americans speak, it sounds like stones dropping in water. I have a hard time understanding, but Hagop reassures me that it will change.

American foods are also very different. They have hot dogs, hamburgers and the strangest, Jell-O. It is soft and colorful like Turkish Delight, but without nuts. Hot dogs are not warmed up dogs, but thin ground pieces of meat like shish kabab and are served with slices of bread that matches its physique. Hamburgers are round slabs of ground meat inside a two round pieces of bread, along with tomatoes and green vegetables. They are like a kebab without the onions. My favorite is Graham Crackers: sweet flat pastry a little bigger than a playing card. A big box costs 5 cents and Hagop and I have one cracker each, with tea, every night. Graham Crackers are tasty, but not as good as Mother's gata.

Of course, at home we mostly eat Armenian food, dolma, lahmajun—Americans call this pizza—supas and so on. My mother-in-law is a good cook, but the food tastes different here. I would like so much to have one of Grandma's supas—the one that "makes the sick run and dead rise." Grandma probably puts some secret ingredient in her supas that makes it better than any other.

Watertown has many beautiful churches. They do not look like Armenian Churches, but some look like the church in Van that the American missionaries had built, but much bigger and prettier. Mrs. Avanian told me that local Armenians are talking about building an Armenian Church in Watertown. She also told me that there is an Armenian Church called Our Savior in a town called Worcester. It is not far from here and we will visit it on one Sunday.

Boston and Watertown are spread on a flat land. There are no mountains here. There is a long river called the Charles River that stretches through Boston and Watertown. Charles River is much bigger than Urpat Creek. It is like the River Arax.

Lianoush would like it here. I wanted to send her a mechanical pencil sharpener. You put the pencil in a metal hole in a round device and it sharpens pencils when you turn the handle. Unfortunately, Mr. Parumian could not take it with him when he traveled to Van because he was sure that it would be taken away by the officials.

Hagop's mother and aunt are both very nice to me and gave me lots of presents. It is starting to feel like home here, but I miss you all so badly. One day when Hagop and I will have money, we would like to buy tickets for you to come here. Hagop says that America is a place to raise children.

I miss Van, Vanalich, the mountains, our home, our garden and most of all, all of you. I have our family picture next to my bed and look at you when I say my prayers every night.

Always your daughter,
Myranoush

I read Myranoush's letter at least thirty times. I should start calling her Myra myself. I guess when I go to America I will be called Lia—not bad at all. I like the Anoush part of my name, though. I wonder if Americans can pronounce Anoush?

I looked at the Atlas that Markos brought from his school and tried to locate Boston. If Polis is one finger span distance from Van, Boston is as far as two hand spans and a lot of ocean water. Myranoush is so far away from us and I miss her so much, but I am glad that she is happy in America. Her new home sounds wonderful.

Mother tried to read the letter in between the lines. She thought that even if Myranoush was not as happy as she wrote, she would keep it secret from us, just because we are so far from her. Armed with her skeptical instinct, she reread the letter herself many times, but could not find the line that would support her suspicion. Her negative attitude about everything irritates me, but made me hesitant about writing to Myranoush about all the things that I would like to discuss with her. I should not overwhelm her with all the chaotic feelings that I have to deal with. I will write her a short letter about how much I miss her and that I would like to visit her in America.

Too bad Mr. Parumian refused to bring the mechanical pencil sharpener. And also, I wonder how much money is 5 cents?

Part Four

The Alarming Events

The Dream

FEBRUARY 17, 1915

I had an odd dream today; it was colorful, just like real life. I was sleeping on the Island of Akhtamar and in the dream an angel came to me. He had big beautiful white wings and a very gentle voice. He introduced himself as Gabriel, and talked to me as if we were old friends and he knew me well. "Lianoush, you should go and tell the adults that the Turks are going to attack Armenians. Armenians should be prepared. God will be with them. You should be brave, pray a lot and you will be saved."

When I woke up, the first thing I checked was what day it is. Grandma Marina says that dreams that come on Sunday nights never come true. Today is Tuesday, I remembered, disappointed. I put on my clothes and ran downstairs. Grandma was knitting and Tavi and Tagi were playing with the yarn. "For God's love, Lianoush, my soul, please take the cats out, they are going to tear up all of my yarn." I let the cats out of the house and came back to Grandma. I was worried that Grandma is too sensitive to hear my dream, even though I was dying to hear her interpretation.

"Grandma, what does it mean, when Gabriel the Angel visits you in your dream?"

"Angels protect you, and what they say is true," she answered without taking her eyes of the sock that was almost done. She was knitting the third pair of socks for Myranoush and Hagop.

"What did the angel say, my soul?" asked Grandma, starting to show a little more interest in my dream.

"Nothing," I answered quickly.

Markos was having breakfast, hard-boiled eggs, salt and lavash. He was cutting the egg into six equal boat shapes, salting those, sprinkling with tarragon and making a perfect lavash wrap. He does this every morning, a real chemist. He overheard my conversation with Grandma and asked cheerfully, "Which one of the angels visited you, Princess?" That is what he calls me, for I am Lianoush the Second.

"It was Gabriel, the angel," I replied and suddenly I lost control of my words and said as fast as I could, "He said the Turks are going to attack Armenians."

Markos stopped chewing, his smile disappeared. He did not say anything, grabbed his hat, stroked my hair and ran out of the house.

 ## Jevdet Bey—New Governor of Van
THE FEBRUARY 19, 1915

Today at school we were told that Van has a new Vali, or Governor, named Jevdet Bey. Prominent Armenians and Turks welcomed him at the Tabriz gate of the City. Jevdet marched into the City escorted with six hundred horsemen. The old Governor, Hasin Tahsin Bey, was transferred to Erzerum. Tahsin Bey had been Vali of Van for two years and once visited our school and talked to us in Turkish. We prepared a nice welcome for him and he was happy with our superintendent.

When Liavart and I got home, Grandpa did not look happy. He could not stop talking about Jevdet Bey's appointment. "This is for a reason. Bad reason. Enver is planning to get rid of us and is sending his bloody brother-in-law." Apparently Jevdet grew up in Van.

"I remember Jevdet when he was a boy; they used to live at the Jidejian's house in the City. Even as a child he was meaninglessly cruel. One time, when he was eleven, he nailed a live dog to a tree."

Grandpa kept repeating, "This is bad news. Tahsin Bey is a decent man, he respects Armenians. The only thing Jevdet Bey is famous for is cruelty."

Enver Pasha is one of the three ministers who had taken over the government of Turkey. He is the Minister of War. The other two are Talaat Pasha, Minister of Interior, and Jamal Pasha, Minister of Marine. The three of those prominent Turks are the head of the government of Young Turks—Ottoman Empire. Grandpa calls them the "three-headed Dragon." So, Jevdet is the brother-in-law of one of the heads of the dragon. Markos said that for his cruelty, Jevdet received the nickname, "Blacksmith." I heard that he was given that name for nailing a horseshoe under people's feet. He was also known to enjoy torturing people and "having fun" seeing people die.

After dinner, Father and Markos went to a meeting at someone's house and came back very late. Men have been leaving home almost every night for meetings, and they look more and more secretive and spend less time with us at home.

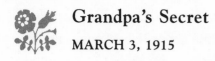

Grandpa's Secret

MARCH 3, 1915

Last night I woke up in the middle of the night feeling cold. I had a dream that it was winter and I fell into the Vanalich. There was a boat, but nobody was in it. Every time I tried to climb into the boat, it would slide away from me. I was trying and trying to cling to the boat, but I could not hold onto its slippery edges. Finally, I woke up. I was covered with cold sweat. The house was freezing because the stove was not started yet. Liavart was breathing rhythmically and quietly. I pulled my wool blanket up to my nose and tried to go back to sleep when I heard footsteps. First, I got scared again, but then I recognized Grandpa's heavy footsteps.

I put my jacket over my nightgown, and without making noise, slipped out of the room. Grandpa was fully dressed and was heading to the outside door. He looked secretive, as if he was hiding something. Actually, he was hiding something under his coat. I was determined to find out what was he doing. Enough of these adult secrets! I followed him to the yard. Grandpa had a shovel and a clay pitcher in his hand, and, as I watched, he started to dig the ground under the big apricot tree. I could hear his heavy breathing; he looked old. He is not doing much digging now, and even though the soil is crumbly and soft from the rains, it was hard for him to dig. I could not stay unnoticed much longer.

"Grandpa, what are you doing?"

"Shhhh, I am hiding some gold for the 'Black Day.'" He took a deep breath. I noticed now that the clay jar was full of yellow gold coins. Not that Black Day again. . . I thought Black Day pertained only to food.

"What do you mean, Grandpa?" I continued questioning him.

"If the Turk attacks our home and takes everything, we will still have some gold that he would not find buried in the yard," he murmured. His gray heavy mustache was bouncing up and down as he spoke.

Grandpa always talks about Turks as if there is only one person—Turk.

Somehow his reasoning did not sound very comforting to me, that we will have gold after the Turks attack our home. One thing is clear to me: that day would be a Black Day.

After he was done burying the pitcher, he looked cheerful as if he had accomplished something important. I helped him to make the place even and unnoticeable. I gave him my word that I won't tell anyone about the night and we went back to bed.

I could not sleep for a long time. Drowning in the Vanalich and then the Black Day's gold were drilling holes in my brain.

 ## The Saddest Birthday
MARCH 24, 1915

Today is the saddest day of my life. It started as usual. Moreover, it was Liavart's twelfth birthday and we were going to celebrate it with a family dinner. Grandpa had Misho skin a lamb, because the winter food storage is almost empty. Grandma cooked the lamb on a slow fire and made a stew. I don't think I want to eat lamb stew ever again.

Everyone was nicely dressed for the dinner. Grandma was wearing her beautiful jewelry, as she always does for such occasions. Gold coins on a chain were covering her forehead and a thick gold chain was adorning her neck. We were sitting at the dinner table ready to say the prayer, when suddenly without knocking, six Turkish soldiers rushed inside the house.

One of the Turkish soldiers screamed, "You filthy Armenians! While Turkey is at war, you are hiding like rabbits and having parties. We have an order to take Armenian men to help the Turkish army to dig trenches." Ice cold shivers ran down my back.

Some Vanetsi men had already been taken to the war as *amele*: labor battalions of the Turkish army. Turks do not want Armenians to have arms and fight in the regular army, but want to use them to dig trenches and clean up after their soldiers. I have heard Father saying that it is humiliating for Armenians to participate in the war as ameles.

Grandma started to sob. Liavart and I followed her example. Mother was standing like a frozen statue. One of the Turks approached Father, "You should come with us. And you," he turned to Markos.

I noticed that Misho suddenly disappeared. I did not hear any doors opening or closing. Markos turned his face to one of the Turks and without looking at him said calmly in Turkish, "I am exempt from the army, I am a school teacher." One of the Turks recognized him. He jerked his head and said something, lowering his voice. Last year, Markos had tutored his son during the summer. Markos was left alone. Father was packing his belongings under the Turkish rifle point. Mother suddenly turned around and before she made a step towards Father, she fainted. Before Father could get to her, one of the

Turks pointed his gun at Father's head. Markar and Ohannes started to scream. Araxi took the boys and rushed upstairs.

"May your heads be buried," Grandma murmured in a hoarse whisper. Most of the Turks know enough Armenian to understand what she said. One of the Turks, with a rusty moustache and red face, grabbed her necklace, then forehead medallions, and pulled them. Some of the pieces of gold fell crumbling on the ground.

"We are going to bury you *gyavours*," chuckled the red-faced Turk, picking up the gold medallions from the ground and pushing them into his pockets. Two other Turks followed his example.

My heart was breaking. Not only were the gendarmes taking Father away, they were also stealing our wealth and mocking us by calling us gyavours—infidels.

They left, taking Father, pushing him with a rifle between his shoulder blades. We were not even allowed to say good-bye to him.

That night I could not sleep. I wanted so badly to fall asleep and see Gabriel the angel.

O, Dear Lord, please take pity on Father and give strength to Mother.

 Ameles

APRIL 2, 1915

Many other Vanetsi men were taken as ameles into Turkish labor battalions from Aygestan and the City. We were told that Jevdet Bey demanded that four thousand men join the Turkish army. Five hundred men, including my Father, had already been taken to the Russian-Turkish front and the Armenian leaders refused to provide any more work forces for the Turkish army. Jevdet Bey was disappointed and angry. Prior to this war, Armenians were never admitted to the Turkish army, but paid a head tax instead. Now they are taken to the army, but are not given any arms. It seems to me that the new Turkish law has two purposes: once men are taken away, the rest of the population was weakened and also Armenian men are not armed so they cannot fight. I remember that Father said how humiliating it is for men to be in an army and not carry arms.

Everyone at our house is frightened and nervous. Grandma has felt ill and stayed in bed since the day Turks left with my father and took her family jewelry. Ohannes cries a lot and tries to hide behind Mother's apron. Grandpa spends most of his day looking out the window and smoking his water pipe. Liavart clutches Tavi, but at times she stares at the wall, meaninglessly, for hours. Father's horse, Sipan, neighs all day. He is constantly shaking his mane and twitching his tail. Even though Markos has taken over Father's responsibilities for feeding and cleaning the horse, Sipan has changed. He seems restless and irritated. Markos even tried to ride him, but Sipan bucked him and did not let Markos get close to the saddle again. Horses have an exceptional sense of smell and are sensitive to the scent of people. Sipan has been looking for Father.

Sipan is about twenty years old. Mother says that he has lived that long only because of Father's care. The whinnying of the horse has been so disruptive that the decision was made for Markos to give it to Poghos Agah, who has a large stable and more experience dealing with horses. Father will bring his horse back when he returns.

The Disturbing News

APRIL 5, 1915

Today at school, all the teachers were acting strangely, as if something is going to happen. Even though we are studying the history of France, the history teacher, Eprem Agah, kept repeating that Armenians have lived in Van for many centuries and our churches and faith have helped us survive. After the second recess, we were sent home and were told not to play in the streets, but to hurry home.

Now that there are only two of us, Liavart and I usually walk in silence. I guess we miss Myranoush, even though she actually never talked much to us. But that was different. Misho has not come back since the day the Turkish gendarmes took Father away. Strangely, Grandpa Panoss does not look surprised or puzzled. I think he knows something that we don't.

It is getting warmer and the trees have started to show small blossoms. I love Van in the spring. Melted snow from the mountains is flooding the streets, overflowing Urpat Creek. Frequently you can hear the splashing of the happy water.

At home things are different, too. Normally at this time of year, Grandpa Panos and Misho visit the mills at least twice a week. Grandpa makes sure that the peasants have been cleaning and drying the mills and if there are any problems, he brings Father's attention to the problems that need to be fixed. But now, the Turks have taken Father away and Misho has mysteriously disappeared. Not only that—Grandpa has not been to the villages since the middle of March because Kurdish tribesman and Turkish gendarmes have been increasingly attacking Christians on the outskirts of Van. We have been hearing some horrible stories about the suffering of the villagers. It is not safe to go to the villages.

Markos has been coming home very late. Araxi spends most of her days at the American Compound with patients. Grandma Marina still is not feeling well and stays in bed a lot. Poor Mother has to take care of Grandma, the boys, and all the cooking and cleaning. She does all this by herself, work which was normally shared by herself, Grandma Marina and Misho. Liavart and I help as much as we can. Tavi and Tagi are the only happy creatures around. They march in and out of the house enjoying the warmth of the spring sun. It seems like they are starting to get along better with the boys.

Part Five

The Siege of Van

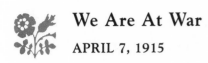

We Are At War

APRIL 7, 1915

Life has changed. We are at war. This is what Markos told us. Jevdet Bey has brought war to the Armenians of Van. He started his war by getting rid of the Armenian leaders of Van. Last Saturday, on April 4, one of the Dashnak party leaders, Ishkhan, was ordered to go to the small town of Shatakh as a mediator to "restore calm and reason." It was a trap. Jevdet Bey gave an order to kill him and the four other Armenians accompanying him.

I knew Ishkhan well. His house was right next to our school and I had frequently seen him getting into a carriage in the mornings. He had short moustache, a beard and willful dark eyes. He was a known political leader and his death was a big blow to Armenians. The other Armenian leader, the Parliament Deputy Arshak Vramian, was arrested. Rumors were spreading that he was killed on a boat on the way to Bitlis.

Aram Manukian, the remaining leader of Dashnak party escaped from an arrest and now has formed the Military Committee of Armenian Self-Defense of Van. The three Armenian parties that were known to disagree on almost everything united to protect the people of Van. The leader of Armenakan party, Armenak Ekarian, will head the Committee with Aram Manukian. The Painter who was not in any party, also joined the Military Committee. Armenians of Van have never been as united as now. However, Turks have more soldiers, arms, ammunition and bombshells than we do. In fact, they have ten times more.

Under the orders of the Military Committee, Armenians from mixed Muslim and Armenian quarters like Norshen Sufla, Norshen Ulia, Karoian and Boyents have been evacuated to Armenian quarters. Many houses of Armenians, along Khach Polan, were turned into fighting positions. Each position has its commander and fighters.

My world suddenly has turned upside down. Our house rules have changed, and the inhabitants of our house have changed. A family of five—Hasmig Khatoun, her daughter-in-law, Vartouhi and her three children from ages three to seven—have come to live with us. Their house was taken over by Turks. Turks took Vartouhi's husband, like my father, as an amele to dig trenches.

Our life was turned into chaos. Grandma was in bed and quiet. Hasmig Khatoun, on the other hand, was sitting on a mindar swaying left and right, muttering pretty much non-stop, "Vai aman, aman, aman, what did you bring on our heads? Vai aman, aman, aman!" She was starting to get on my nerves. Usually women do that at the funerals. I offered her a cup of rose tea; she refused, but then settled for a cup of coffee. Shortly after finishing her coffee, she continued her ritual, but not such in an annoying way.

Their three children looked extremely frightened, so I tried to cheer them up. Ohannes looked very scared, too. Little children could not sleep, so I sang Grandma's lullaby for them.

Sleep little child, lay down your head
Morning comes soon, lay down your head
Sleep little child, have sugar sweet dreams
Relax in rest, under watchful eyes of angels

Wake little child, happy to play
Wake little child, start a new day
But now sleep little child, lay down your head
Morning comes soon, lay down your head

The Siege

APRIL 12, 1915

We haven't been out of the house for two days. The bombardment started two days ago and stopped only for few hours each night. Markos and Araxi have not been home for days. Araxi is working at a hospital that was opened in Arark quarter, at the Totovent's house. Markos is preparing cartridges for rifles and explosive powder for bombs at an Armenian home that was converted into a gun powder factory.

The local newspaper is still getting printed and we are getting a copy almost every day, bringing the news from the front. The Military Committee forbade any alcohol drinking. Grandpa said that he is toasting for fighters and kept drinking his arak.

Our house was hit twice by Turkish artillery, luckily without much damage. The Turks took over the British Consulate and positioned their artillery there. The British Consulate was my favorite building in Aygestan. Now shells are being fired on the Armenian quarters from its verandas.

Vanetsis from the City are completely isolated from the Aygestan and are fighting their own battle. Turks are controlling the road from Aygestan to the City. Rare Armenian soldiers would dare to cross Haykavank and get to the City to bring some news from the Armenians stranded in the occupied City. Homes of the wealthy Armenians in the City are turned into military posts. Armenian fighters are concentrated in those posts.

The Turkish army has three major advantages against Armenians. They have lots of arms and ammunition, an unrestricted food supply, and communication with the outside world from where they could get anything they need. Besides, most of the Turks are trained to fight and are part of the regular Turkish Army. The majority of Armenians, on the other hand, are civilians; merchants, shopkeepers, teachers, poets and artists. In a very uneven combat, Vanetsi Armenians are trying to withstand the Turkish attacks.

"Black Day's" Food
APRIL 17, 1915

The Military Committee ordered all the people to move downstairs. It is no longer safe on the second floor. The twelve of us are living downstairs in the living room. Water is a big problem, because someone has to run outside to the spring and bring it home. Mother says she is the only one allowed to do it, but I think I can do it, too.

The days feel longer and seem to go on forever. Mother is having a hard time feeding us all. Sacrificing herself for others is Mother's everyday job. I don't think she eats much, if at all. For others, she is rationing the food very strictly. We are allowed one lavash wrap with cheese for breakfast, two for lunch, a bowl of yogurt or supas and lentils for dinner. Before the war, every time when we had to eat lentils or beans Grandpa used to announce, "We are eating a poor man's dinner today." Of course, now he does not say a word. We eat in silence and are thankful for any food Mother gives us. Our supply of food in the maran is getting scarce, for it is April, and we also have more people to feed.

For the first time since I remember, we had to use the food stash labeled "Black Day's Food." Moreover, for the last weeks I understood what the Black Day is. We are living it now. We can't get out of the house and our food supply is running very short.

I thought about the pitcher of gold buried in the yard and asked Grandpa if it is time to take it out. Grandpa looked annoyed and whispered so no one could hear us, "This is a Black Day, but there is no use for gold." Then he continued, "You can't buy food with it, you can't even buy guns with it." Guns are in short supply and were changing hands only when the previous owner was killed. Grandpa, who was always against arms, recently changed his opinion and wanted to get a rifle. He told Markos that he is the only man at home and should have a gun in case the Turks attack our house. Markos could not get him a rifle either, but he gave him an old pistol and Grandpa was keeping it under his pillow. I had to agree with Grandpa that there is no use for gold now.

We have not seen Tavi and Tagi for days, since the bombardment of Aygestan started. They ran out of the house one day when Mother went outside for water and never came back. Mother did not let me to go outside and look for them. Van cats don't like noise. I hope they are hiding someplace where there is peace and quiet.

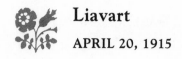

Liavart

APRIL 20, 1915

This has been a horrible day for us. I don't even know where to start.

Mother finally allowed me to go outside and bring water. Today when she was in the maran, Liavart disobeyed Mother and ran to the yard. Just then a bombshell fell in our yard, when Liavart was trying to fetch some water. The flying shell struck the earth and created an explosion that broke the windows upstairs. Liavart was thrown about 20 yards from the place that she was, towards the barn. Then the ground stopped shaking. We all ran out of the house. Liavart was lying unconscious, covered with dirt and gunpowder. Mother's body was trembling, but tears were coming without noise. We picked Liavart up and brought her home. She was very pale. We put her head on a pillow, her eyes were closed, but we could see her breathing.

My heart was beating very fast and I was shivering. "I should go get Araxi, she knows what to do."

"I cannot lose two of my daughters in one day," moaned Mother.

"It is only two blocks away from here. I won't go through the open field, I will avoid the fire. I will be fine; Liavart needs help."

I ran toward the Totovents' house in Arark quarter, where the hospital was set up. I could hear the whistling bullets and the thud of the bombs exploding somewhere else. I got to the hospital safely and found Araxi. She looked exhausted and ten years older than two weeks ago. After she heard what happened, she ordered two boys with a gurney to follow us. The four of us got home safely. Liavart now had opened her eyes, but was not able to move her left side. Araxi got close to her, kissed her forehead, stroked her hand and said, "She should see a doctor." Mother was giving her some sugar water and was constantly stroking her hair or kissing her forehead. Araxi's helpers carefully lifted Liavart onto the gurney. Liavart's face grimaced with pain.

I saw the expression on the Mother's face when she was looking at Araxi. "Please, save her," her eyes were saying.

Grandpa Panos looked like a wounded animal. I could see that the fire of life had seemed to burn down in his eyes. I had never seen him moving his worry beads so slowly, as if each bead weighed a ton.

That night, the same two boys brought Liavart back. She'd had a piece of shell removed from her left hip, but also had a fracture in the pelvis. She has to be in bed for some time. Araxi would come to check on her and change the bandage every day, but Liavart can stay at home. She brought some liquid that we are supposed to give Liavart when she is in too much pain.

O, Lord, help Liavart to get better, she is only 12 years old. What if she limps for the rest of her life?

 The Heroic Fight of Vanetsis
APRIL 22, 1915

The Turks have been surrounding the Aygestan in a circle and have been firing at the Armenian quarters from all sides, day and night. The shells were coming from Hadji Bekr Barracks from the south, from Toprak Kale Barracks from the north, from Hamud Agah Barracks and British Consulate from the center. Armenian soldiers built trenches all around Aygestan. Defense walls have been building during nights under a continuous cannonade. Araxi was telling us the stories from the front.

Armenians of Van used all kinds of creative tricks. Women were fighting along with men. And those were the Vanetsi women, who thought that the only purpose for a woman is to go to school, wear clean clothes, marry, have children, raise them, and nag men.

There was such a shortage of ammunition that some brave Armenian women watched as unexploded bombs would tear the ground. They had pitchers of water in their hands and because the fuses on the bombs were cut long, they had time to run to the shell and pour cold water on the burning fuse. Then, once the bomb cooled down, the explosive powder was removed from the shell and taken to the plant, where jewelers, tinsmiths and chemistry teachers reloaded the powder into cartridges. Markos was working in that factory.

Some women walked from house to house and collected all the Singer sewing machines they could find. They started a factory to make clothes for the fighters.

Many stories were beyond imagination. One night, Armenians took a small dog and tied a lantern to it. The Turks saw the moving lantern, thinking that it was a group of Armenians, opened fire at the height of a man. In the other Turkish positions, the soldiers heard gunshots and thought that the Armenians were shooting at the Turks. Thousands of bullets and kegs of gunpowder were wasted, and the Turks never found out that the dog safely came back to his owner.

All night, Armenian soldiers were digging underground tunnels to get to important Turkish positions. The Turks were doing the same thing. One time, the wall between the tunnels collapsed and the fight continued underground.

A young girl, Sevo, who is only twelve, was running between trenches and taking important messages. She was awarded a "Cross of Honor." I admire Sevo for her bravery. Many high school boys, including my cousin, Agassi, were running like Gavroches* through the whistling bullets and fetching the unused bullets for fighters.

The music band was marching around under cannonade and playing high-spirited tunes like *Our Fatherland* to cheer up the Armenian soldiers. Most of the band musicians were high school boys. I knew some of them. Even through the cannonade, many times a day we could hear the tunes of the fanfare.

Jevdet Bey reportedly announced, "This country will remain either for the Armenians or Turks, but it is impossible that the two can coexist." The Vanetsi Armenians are fighting for their lives. If the Turks win, they are not going to spare anyone. I wanted to do something useful, but Mother said that she couldn't manage the house without me. I am kind of upset with Liavart. Couldn't she have been more careful? Now I have to stay home and read letters and stories to her to

---

*Gavroch: a boy from *Les Miserables* by Hugo.

keep Mother from losing her mind. I am sad and mad, but what can I do?

I frequently think about Father. Is he still alive? None of us dare ask a question aloud about him. What Vartouhi told me gave me cold chills. Armenian men, who were used by the Turkish army to dig trenches, were shot afterwards and thrown in those trenches. When I close my eyes, I see Father buried under many heavy bodies.

Could he maybe have escaped? I want him so much to escape and come back home. Father was taken away from us, but I feel even worse for him. He was deprived of the right to protect his own family. If I shut my eyes, I see his calm familiar face. His calm and disciplined attitude is what I need now. I need to raise my spirit and give hope to everyone and myself.

Dear merciful God, look at us, help us, we can't do this without Your help.

Is This Land Cursed?
APRIL 24, 1915

The British Consulate was blazing in fire all day today. The smoke was rising into the sky, higher than the smoke from many other small and middle size fires in Aygestan. The night before, Vanetsi defenders managed to inject the walls of the Consulate with gasoline. A hail of bullets shot at the Consulate started a huge fire and Turkish soldiers were running for their lives.

The Turks bombarded the Russian Consulate during the first days of the siege. Supposedly, no one was in the building.

The Consul and his staff left soon after the Turkish government entered into the war on Germany's side against the Russians in the fall of last year.

The Italian Consulate placed white flags all over its building, confirming their neutrality and asking Jevdet and Armenians to refrain from hitting their buildings. The American Premises also have the white flags, and so far, are staying neutral without being involved in the battle. We have heard that Jevdet Bey wanted to place Turkish soldiers at the American compound "to protect Americans from savage Armenians," but Dr. Ussher categorically refused the "thoughtful" proposal of the Governor. If the Turks get on the American Premises, they will be shooting at us from the southeast, too.

The Turks set the Market of Van on fire. The beautiful Market in the City. Just like the City, the Market was very old. And now it was burning. Shops, cafes, bookstores, libraries, theatres, churches, everything was on fire. The City had many underground old tunnels. Some of the tunnels built by the Queen Shamiram carried water, and when bombs hit them the water gushed out. Fire and water were everywhere—but there was not enough water to quench the fire.

Late at night, I ran outside to bring some water for Grandma. For a short time it was quiet. I looked at the sky. This time of the year, the sky is covered with stars, but now the sky was dark, gloomy and empty—no stars or moon in the sky. They have left Van.

I thought about the Urartian Kingdom and what happened to it. Urartians were strong; they had powerful fortresses built on heights, hard to conquer. But that did not help them survive the enemy attacks. Assyrians suffered the same fate. The Powerful Queen Shamiram's country disappeared into the history books and Assyrians do not have a homeland anymore. No country, no homeland. Is this land cursed? Is it our turn now? Will the same thing happen to us Armenians? Are we going to disappear from the maps into history and leave just our writings and churches as a memory of us?

I thought about the dream I had several weeks ago, when Gabriel the angel came to me predicting all that is happening to us. It seems that dream was a long time ago. So many things have happened since then. Dreams are messages from someone, someone important. Grandma says that, and I agree with her. I distinctly remember; Gabriel the angel said that Turks will attack us, and that we have to be very strong and we will survive. Is this true? Will we survive? How long can we stand against the Turkish plan to exterminate us?

Where are you, my Angel?

 ## The Fearless Levon Agah
APRIL 27, 1915

Despite the siege and persistent bombardment, Levon Agah continued to visit us frequently, bringing news from the battlefield. According to him, yesterday the Turkish troops captured the Varag Monastery, where many nearby villagers had found shelter and refuge. It was very bad news. First, because thousands of Armenian families lost their shelter; but also, the Turks are winning more of the Armenian positions and surrounding us in a wider circle. Levon Agah told us that he wanted to be a soldier and fight against the Turks, but the

Military Committee denied him because of his age. What he really told us was that they did not have enough guns to trust them to older people. Today when he came, I told him that he is very brave to walk in Aygestan where you could be hit by a stray bullet any time. He has not been laughing recently, but this time he did.

"Lianoush, my soul, I am not afraid of anyone or anything. The Turks took everything from me a long time ago. All I had was my shop, and now it is gone, too. Did you see that big red fire and the smoke coming from the Market? Those were my kilims. Death does not scare me, only life does." His eyes looked wild and his face was contorted with sarcasm. I did not know what to say in response and was thankful to Grandpa for intervening in the awkward situation.

"Lianoush, go to the maran and bring some lavash, cheese and arak." I was happy to run to the maran and get them. The empty shelves of the maran did not make me feel any better, but still, facing Levon Agah was much worse. I could still smell the basturma, even though the last of it was eaten a long time ago. When all this is over I would like to eat eggs with basturma, I thought as I left the mostly empty maran.

When Levon Agah left that day, I asked Grandma about what happened to his family. I learned a lot about Levon Agah, and not only about him.

Levon Agah had a very beautiful wife. Her name was Seeroon. According to Grandma, there was an evil eye on her family clan and she brought it to Levon Agah with her. Many men wanted to marry Seeroon, but he was the lucky one.

Seeroon was from a well-known, wealthy family in Vaspu-rakan, who owned many orchards. People of Sultan Hamid killed Seeroon's parents, brothers and sisters and destroyed their orchards. After she found out about her family, she became very ill.

Seeroon and Levon Agah had three boys. For many years, Levon Agah took care of his ill wife and three boys until Seeroon died about 13 years ago. Levon Agah never married again and raised his sons alone. One of his sons was helping him in his business, but, one day when he was bring-ing rugs from Polis, he was suffocated in the hot carriage full of rugs.

His other two sons did not want to be in the rug business and were active in the Dashnak party. One of them was Tigran. I heard that name before, most recently when I was eavesdropping and learned that Araxi was engaged to him.

About seven years ago, two Armenians from the Da-shnak party argued because of a woman, and one of them, Davo, who became extremely distraught as a result of the argument, reported to the Turkish gendarmes the hideouts where the Armenians were storing arms. The Armenian houses were besieged and the Turks searched the homes. Tigran and his brother were killed while resisting the Turkish gendarmes. I had heard before about Davo's treason as a hor-rible event, but did not know how much Levon Agah, and also Araxi, suffered from it. I remember what Hagop said, when he came to ask for Myranoush's hand. Turks kill us because we are Arme-nian. No one can stop the Turks. They killed us before, they are doing it again. But how can we all get to America?

The Late Night Guest
APRIL 29, 1915

We had a strange guest today. After darkness fell, somebody knocked on the door. We were terrified even though something was familiar about the way the door was knocked. Grandpa looked at me, which meant I had to run and get the pistol from under his pillow. But before I could move, we heard, "Lianoush, Liavart open the door, it is me, Misho."

We opened the door and there was Misho, but he was very hard to recognize. He was wearing a woman's long black dress and a funny headscarf. As much as I was startled, I could not keep from laughing. His moustache did not go well with his dress. We were all happy to see him. Grandpa hobbled around Misho looking happy and childish. His face was saying matter-of-factly, "I knew he would be back."

Misho had a big, dusty bag in his hand. Still standing next to the door he said, "I was very worried about you, but could not come. The Turkish government announced that they would kill any Kurd or Turk who helps Armenians. Today I was at the village of Membar. It is empty; all Armenian villagers were either killed or deported. The small granary had few bags of flour from what was supposed to have been delivered to us in March. I brought you one bag of flour, I could not carry more."

We are running very low on flour and it was very good news for us. Mother looked thankfully at him. Grandpa asked Mother to bring some bread, cheese and arak. For the first time, Misho was treated as a guest. We were told to go to bed. Now that we are all sleeping downstairs in the living room, I could watch them. Misho said he couldn't stay for a long time, but Grandpa had a lot of questions for him. They talked for about an hour. I was trying to make out what he was telling to Grandpa and Mother. All I heard was that Kurds were promised by Jevdet's government that they could move into Armenian homes as their own, once all the Armenians are killed or deported.

Misho did not want to move into Armenian homes. He thought that Armenian Vanetsis had owned their homes for generations and should stay in their homes. As for himself, Misho wants to be a shepherd, just like his father. He wants to lead the flock of sheep to the beautiful meadows in the mountains. I did not know that Misho's dream was to follow his father's steps. I realized that we never asked him what he wants to do. In our house, he was always told what to do.

Misho left our home after he said goodbye to all of us. For the first time I saw tears in Grandpa's eyes. Misho was like a son to him.

As a reward for killing Armenians, Kurds are promised our homes. Vanetsis should not let this happen.

Dear Lord, please help us.

 ## The Refugees
APRIL 30, 1915

For the last two days, Armenians from the surrounding villages have been pouring into Aygestan. At first, everyone was happy to see that some of the villagers survived the Turkish atrocities in the neighboring villages. But that was Jevdet's new trick. After killing all the men, the women, children and elderly were channeled to Aygestan. Jevdet is trying to starve us to death. Thousands of people, weak, sick, ragged and starving, are entering Aygestan after they were forced to abandon their homes in the villages. The poor villagers had the dreadful experience of losing their homes and loved ones and now are at the mercy of the Vanetsis who, themselves, have been under siege for weeks. The faces of refugees are grimaced with pain, disease and hunger. Many refugees have found shelter at the American Premises.

Mother let several families into our barn, Grandpa's old house. We still have some animals left; most of them were lost during the bombardment. The sheep did not produce any milk but we could not kill the animals. First, no one could stay outside for long enough to complete that awful task, and secondly, there are no men available to do it. So, we have to feed them. We are completely out of meat, but still have some tarekh, beans, and lentils in the maran. Thanks to Misho, we also have a bag of flour. The Military Committee issued some orders to distribute the food supply fairly, but we are considered "wealthy" and, therefore, are not getting anything.

Mother cooked pots of lentils and beans and took them to the barn. I went with her and tried to help to wash and clean the children and elderly. They were four girls and two boys, too thin and fatigued for me to guess their ages. We did not talk much to each other, as if we did not know each other's language. I brought a brush and started to brush the girl's hair. The bristles of the brush pulled dozens of lice from a little girl's hair. I had seen lice before, but not this many. I made a small fire and threw the lice in it. The children liked the crackling noise the lice made hitting the fire. That cheered up the children and they let me brush their hair, too.

They came one by one to me saying, "me too." Mother put a large bucket of water outside. The days are getting sunnier and the water warmed up easily. I used the water to wash up the children's heads, faces and hands. Mother brought some old clothes and we threw away all the torn and filthy ones.

After they ate, the children started to play *karkutik*, a game with small rocks. They look very comfortable in our barn. After all, it is not very different from what their homes used to be. Mother gave them couple of old kilims to cover the floor and some old jackets to cover themselves at night. Exhausted, they fell asleep at their new home.

That night when Araxi came home to check on Liavart, I told her about the lice. She told me that I should be very careful. Lice bring a deadly disease called typhus.

The Angel
MAY 1, 1915

A bullet hit Markos today while he was taking cartridges to the fighters. He was hit in the left shoulder, not far from his heart. The bullet could have killed him. When he was taken to the hospital, Araxi happened to be the one to meet the gurney and the escort. We heard that Araxi was very brave and acted as if Markos was just another soldier she had to care for. Araxi had seen soldiers dying and she was grateful for Markos's life. She held his hands while Dr. Ussher extracted the bullet. As always, Dr. Ussher started his surgery with a prayer.

"Markos was very lucky. There was probably an Angel watching over him," he commented after the surgery. Markos will stay at the hospital until he is able to walk. After the surgery, Markos was disoriented and could not recognize where he was. He was constantly calling for his mother and was talking to her like a little boy, as if she were right there. Araxi was putting cold towels on his forehead and stroking his curly hair. He was out of danger, but it will take several days before he is released from the hospital.

I think Markos's mother was the Angel who saved his life.

 ## We Are Saved
MAY 3, 1915

All last night we could not sleep from the unremitting cannonade. The Turks have intensified the bombardment of the Armenian positions and houses in Aygestan. Full of fear, we were listening to the whistle of the approaching shells, waiting tensely to hear where it would explode. Miraculously, no shell hit our house. Mother said that it was a night of death and destruction. Later, today, we found out to our surprise that many shells were intended to hit the American Compound. That had never happened before.

This morning Grandma was in some dim world, where she was happy and talking to her late father. The rest of us were wondering about the sudden rest and silence in the cannonade.

Suddenly, Van became quite and peaceful. What happened? Did everyone get killed and the Turks are now searching houses? We were locked in our small world. Even children stopped making noise.

Then we heard pounding on the door. "Open the door! We are saved! The Turks are gone!" It was my cousin, Agassi, but to me it was like the arrival of God Himself.

Agassi looked thin, unkempt and exhausted, but his face was glowing with happiness. It was not a joke, we are saved. The Turks loaded their families on the boats and sailed away towards Bitlis. The siege is over and we Vanetsis are saved.

Grandpa was the happiest. "I told you Byzantines, Arabs, Seljuks, Persians also tried to conquer Van, but Van is for Vanetsi Armenians and will always be. They can cut our branches, but never pull us from the roots!" Grandpa said proudly.

Bah! Five minutes ago we were sure Van would be destroyed, and now we are bragging Vanetsis again!

Now the Turkish positions are blazing. The barracks of Toprak Kale, Hamud Agah and Hadji Bekr are all on fire. The twenty-six days of the siege have changed Van a lot. Many houses and churches are ruined, gardens and trees are burnt to coals. Aygestan looks unrecognizable. The poplar tree with the crane nest, or whatever is left from it, is smoking, surrounded by the other trees that had been caught in the fire and now are charred from flames.

Even the American compound is badly ruined by shells. The last cannons were aimed at the Americans. The beautiful, three story building of the American Hospital where many Armenians, Turks and Kurds were treated before the war, has been turned into ruins by Turkish bombardment.

Jevdet Bey did not forgive Dr. Ussher's reluctance to have Turkish soldiers on his premises.

But, we are free and alive!

Araxi came for a short time and told us her side of the story. From the house where the hospital is, you can see Lake Van. Early morning, dozens of boats started to depart from Avants to Tatvan, the port near Bitlis. First, no one could understand what was happening. Are Turks getting more help? But the boats were sailing from Van. Finally, artillery stopped. The Turks, with all their army and their cruel commander, Jevdet Bey, were running away from Van! I would like to write the last sentence over and over again!

Later, we found out the reason for the Turkish escape. The Russian army was approaching Van and has already taken over Erzerum, Kars and Igdir. Several messengers, some of them young boys, were sent to inform the Russians and the Armenian Volunteer Battalion in the Russian army that Van is stranded and the Armenians of Van are on the verge of extermination. Most of the messengers were killed or captured by the Turks, but luckily, some bypassed the Turks and delivered the message.

Part Six

The Aftermath of The War

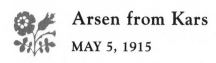

Arsen from Kars

MAY 5, 1915

The Armenian volunteers and the Russian Army marched into Van today. Thousand of these troops poured into Aygestan and the City. The Armenian soldiers were singing *Our Fatherland*.

Our Fatherland, you have been
Chained for so many years,
But now with the help of your sons' sacred blood
You are freed.

The artillery that was overtaken from the escaping Turks now was firing into the air welcoming our lifesavers. Armenian Volunteers and the Russian Army led by General Nikolaev were entering Van. Despite the fires and destruction, Vanetsis had bouquets of red and white flowers for the soldiers who were marching on the streets of Van. We were happily cheering for these brave men. Hurray for our heroes! If not for these soldiers, we would have lost our lives and our land.

An Armenian soldier rode his horse by our house, greeting us, "My country's brave people, God was with you," he said. Then he turned to the boys and offered them to jump on the horse. Ohannes ran away, but Markar came forward.

The man was wearing a uniform and leather boots. He had thick moustache and a big wool hat on his head. His shiny rifle was pointing into the air. He introduced himself as Arsen from Kars, then picked Markar and put him on the horse. "You are brave, son, and one day you will defend our country," he said. Markar beamed proudly. That moment I noticed how much he looks like my father. Mother ran into the house and brought some bread and wine. "Enjoy brother, we are grateful to you for saving our lives." And then she asked exactly what was on my mind. "Have you seen a Vanetsi man by the name Theos Beglarian? He was taken away by Turks as an amele two months ago." The man thought for a second and then answered, "I have not, but there are many Armenians who escaped from the Turkish labor battalions and joined the Armenian forces in the Russian Army. I hope you will hear from him soon." I suddenly felt a surge of hope. In excitement I ran into the house to tell Liavart what just happened.

Later in the evening, we heard Russian soldiers singing around the campfires. Their songs are very different from Armenian songs. They sound almost like a choir, but the tunes are unfamiliar, some of them sound like lullabies.

Dear Lord, thank you for these people, for their courage and spirit.

 ## The End of The Siege
MAY 8, 1915

Even though most of the fighting is over, there are still some fires here and there and a few Turks are still fighting. Our extended family is alive and safe. Tutunjian's home that was used as one of Armenian positions in the City was badly damaged, but everyone was alive. Some relatives came to visit Liavart. She is doing much better and even starting to attempt to walk with a cane. Not everyone was that lucky.

The City was totally ruined. The famous Market of Van was set on fire and all the shops were destroyed. Many Armenian families were killed or burned alive in their own homes. Hermine's family survived, thanks to Zeina's father. Even though Jevdet announced that any Turk who would give refuge to an Armenian family would be executed, Zeina's father kept my aunt's family for 26 days in his basement. They did not see daylight for 26 days! Early May 3, Zeina's father and his family packed and left the City. They locked the house from the outside and told Aunt Victoria to wait in the basement until the fight was over. A shell hit the house later on the same day. The house caught fire. Aunt Victoria's family thought that it was the end. They ran out of the house and, holding hands, ran all the way to Haykavank, which is a deserted area between the City and the Aygestan. Neither Turks nor Armenians were aiming at that area because no one lived there. After the dark came and it was obvious that the fighting was fading down, they reached Aygestan.

Not all the stories turned out so well. We heard that Levon Agah was killed yesterday while fighting face to face with Turks. He had finally managed to get hold of a rifle and with vengeance attacked the Hadji Bekr Barracks, one of the last Turkish positions. Shortly after Levon Agah was shot, Armenians took over the barracks. One of the Armenian fighters pulled Levon Agah from the battlefield and tried to call for help. Levon Agah's last words were, "Son, don't bother, I am the last one of my family. I have nothing to live for, and what more can I ask than fighting for Van and dying for it, the next place for me is Paradise." Those were his last words and he faded with a smile on his face.

To my surprise, Grandpa did not show a lot of emotions when he heard about his friend's death. Is he emotionally exhausted? Levon Agah was his childhood pal and soul mate. The only thing I heard from him was a murmur, "Van in this life, Paradise in next."

The Dead City

JUNE 1, 1915

After the Russian Army arrived in Van and we were liberated, Armenians of Van started to rebuild their homes, whenever it was possible to rebuild. Several days after the Turkish escape, the villagers returned to villages and people from mixed quarters of Aygestan returned to their homes. The only man in our household is Grandpa. We have not heard from my Father. Misho probably will never come back. Markos is better, even though he still carries his arm in a sling. He is very busy with his responsibilities with the new government of Van. Mother and I are trying to patch the second floor damage that happened during the bombardment. Grandpa is giving us valuable instructions, but is not interested in any hands-on help.

For the first time in many centuries, Van is in the hands of Armenians and an Armenian Government is leading the City of Van. Vanetsis are thrilled with these new, exciting, historic events. The schools are not going to start for another two months, so Markos is working for the Defense Ministry of the new Government led by Aram Manukian, who led the heroic defense of Van and is now called Aram Pasha.

The City is so badly damaged that it is impossible to bring it back to life. St. Petros and St. Poghos and other Armenian churches are almost entirely leveled to the ground. Topchu Plaza and the famous market are unrecognizable. On the last days of the siege, many buildings, Turkish or Armenian, were put on fire. Levon Agah's store with its colorful kilims is gone. Poor Levon Agah. Even if he were alive, he would not have been able to rebuild his store.

The beautiful ancient city of Van is turned into a pile of rubbish. The remnants of the gates and the walls surrounding the City, built by Queen Shamiram are destroyed not by earthquake, but by humans.

For thousands of years, this city attracted visitors and was a home to kings and queens, monks and imams, men and women who spoke different languages. Gardens, temples, and churches that were planted and erected by Urartians, Queen Shamiram, King Gagik I and many others were destroyed in 26 days. And only the Rock of Van is still here, casting its shadow over the ruined city. Humans did not built it and they could not destroy it. The indestructible Urartian Fortress escaped the fire and is still standing erect on top of the Rock. The Fortress on the Rock is watching the dead City at its feet. My heart is aching for the beautiful City. The fairy tale City is destroyed. No one will rebuild it. How can anyone know that the same thing is not going to happen again?

I thought about the mythological Mher who locked himself in the cave behind the rock of Toprak Kale and declared that he will come out to destroy or free the world. Evil happened to Urartians. Evil happened to Van before and it is happening again. Mher is not coming out any time soon.

And only the lonely, snow-white Van cats are wandering in the empty plains of the ruined City.

Countess Alexandra Tolstoy

JUNE 5, 1915

The Red Cross joined the Russian Army in the Aygestan. Countess Alexandra Tolstoy, the daughter of Leo Tolstoy, who is the author of *War and Peace*, joined the American missionaries. Araxi met the Countess and spoke highly of her.

I am very excited and want to write a letter to Myranoush telling about the famous writer's daughter in Van. The Red Cross and American missionaries are taking care of the remaining Turks in the area. The majority of Turks fled Van, but about one thousand women, children and elders were left behind. Americans and the Red Cross are on the side of those who are suffering, hungry or wounded. During the siege, they were taking care of thousands of Armenians and for that they fell into major disfavor with Jevdet Bey. His last attacks were aimed at Americans. Now that Armenians are safe and could take care of themselves, missionaries are caring for Turks.

I guess I am not angry with the Countess or Americans for taking care of Turks. After all, these are not the same people that were trying to exterminate us one month ago. These are helpless children and women. In any case, Araxi and other Armenian nurses stopped working for the American Hospital and work at the new Armenian Hospital.

Just like in Leo Tolstoy's book, *War and Peace*, times change, and peace always comes after war. But is this a final peace for us? After all, Turkey is still at war with Russia and Jevdet is still alive. He lives in Bitlis now, and as far as we know, he will be a danger to Armenians as long as he lives.

And not only Jevdet. The three-headed dragon; Enver, Talaat and Jamal, are continuing their plan to exterminate the whole Armenian population and make Turkey for Turks only. News is coming from other parts of Turkey about how Armenians are forced to leave their homes and become refugees. Women, children and elders have been forced to march through deserts to the countries bordering Turkey. Many Armenians are killed. Many are dying from starvation and diseases.

But in Van we have hope. We have peace. Life is slowly normalizing.

 ## I Want My Cats!

JUNE 22, 1915

It is getting warm outside; early summer is beautiful in Van. Grandma is starting to recover from prolonged illness. Liavart is now walking with a cane. Every day, I hoped so badly that Tavi and Tagi would come back. After all, they are smart cats and should be able to find our house, their home. I have kept putting milk and yogurt next to the front door hoping they will smell it and return, but there is no sign of my precious cats. Cats don't like noise of the cannonade, smoke or fire. The only place in Vaspurakan that was spared from war is the island of Akhtamar. I know the Van cats are good swimmers. Frightened from all the fighting, the cats probably escaped to the island of Akhtamar.

When I asked Markos to take me to the island to look for the cats, he gave me a blunt look and sighed, "Sure, once we have helped humans and secured our country, we will look for your cats." Then he noticed the desperate look on my face and continued, "There are many homeless cats in the City, would you like me to bring one for you?"

But I want my cats back!

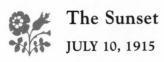

The Sunset

JULY 10, 1915

Markos and I went to Artamet today to check on our cottage and the garden. The village is badly ruined but some people have returned to their houses and are trying to restore their properties. The majority of the villagers were forced to move to either Russia or Persia.

Markos still has his left arm in the sling, so I have been doing most of the work. With his right arm, Markos tried to help me as much as he could. We were there quite long and did not notice that it started to get dark. We were both tired, but Markos looked at me and said, "We should go watch the sunset on the Lake." I was sure that Mother would not approve of Markos's idea to watch the sunset when we have so many chores to do, but I followed him in silence. The lake is only few blocks away from our cottage.

There were no major fires in Artamet, so I was admiring the apple orchards that are heavily loaded with fruit. The apples are still green and just a touch of red is starting to show on the shiny, round surface of the fruit. Artamet apples are famous for their taste and their looks, and are usually picked in September or early October. Some say that you can look through the Artamet apples and see the seeds. Personally, I like the unripe green apples while they are still sour, crunchy and slightly biting. I picked an apple and dug my teeth into the hard fruit, the sour juice filled my mouth and I grimaced. When I opened my eyes we were at the lake. Markos was not moving, his eyes were stuck on the lake.

There is nothing like the colors of that sunset. Regular words can not describe it. The big, heavy, round, bright yellow-orange sun was slowly sliding down toward the northern rocky edge of the island of Akhtamar. A bloodshot mountain of light, the remnant of the dying day, was slowly getting smaller and following the disappearing sun. A blue stripe of sky was separating the setting sun from the dark black endless horizon. The waters of Lake Van were quiet, without a breeze. The lake looked frozen. The water was dark, almost black with a shining array from the reflection of the setting sun. We had to hurry home.

The sunset, it's the time when the sun leaves us,
In rapture and bliss,
The sunset, it's before the sunrise,
Where the new day lies.
The sunset is when butterflies say good-bye,
"Farewell, farewell," they cry.
The sunset is when the sounds fade away,
The moon comes up,
Her stare has gone astray.
"Farewell, farewell," I think to my surprise.

Part Seven

Farewell to Van

The Order of The Military Committee

JULY 18, 1915

Today, we Armenians of Van were told that we should leave Van. That is an order of the Military Committee, which is the Government of Van. General Nikolaev and the Russian Army are retreating back to Russia. They are following the orders of the Russian Czar. It is not safe for us to stay here. Jevdet will be back soon. He proved to us during the siege that no one will be forgiven. All we have is two days to pack all our belongings, or I should say some of our household, and go to the Caucasus. It is our turn to become refugees.

In a trunk that Markos brought from Polis, I packed clothes for Liavart and myself and helped mother with packing for the boys and the household stuff. Markos brought a carriage, and our only mule and two donkeys will pull it. We were told that Father's horse, Sipan, died during the siege. Liavart, Grandma, the twins and Grandpa will have a place to sit in the carriage on the blankets next to the food and household possessions. The rest of us will walk alongside the carriage.

Markos was packing his butterfly collection. He said that it is his most important belonging. Mother looked startled, almost disgusted, but did not say a word. Markos still cannot use his left arm fully, so I had to assist him too. I remembered the days when Markos was taking us on butterfly hunts. So many things have changed since those happy days.

Grandpa behaved very strangely all day. On the one hand he has reverted to something like his old self, very stubborn and self-confident. On the other hand, he looked like he has something peculiar on his mind and looked ridiculously triumphant and happy about it. While everybody else was working trying to pack and be ready for the morning, he was looking out the window, smoking his pipe and intensely moving his worry beads, almost throwing the beads back and forth when he was getting to the edges. Not very surprising, because that is what most of the Armenian men do anyway. He called me and asked me to dig the pitcher of gold and hide it in the carriage and take it out when we get to Russian Armenia. I thought that we should discuss it with Mother and told her about it. Certainly, in my mind this was again a Black Day. Within the last five months, I have learned to understand perfectly well what Black Day means.

The soil was very hard and I had to dig all around the apricot tree until I finally found the pitcher. I gave the pitcher to my Mother. She did not even look inside as if the pitcher was just full of useless rocks and not shining gold. She ordered me to slip the gold into the wool blankets. I opened small holes in the blankets and one by one forced the gold coins inside, then I sewed the holes closed. We did not have much use for gold in Van, but maybe we will in Russian Armenia.

I picked a lot of the grapes and pomegranates even though they are not fully ripe. Mother says that we could use the grapes and the pomegranate seeds instead of water during our journey. It is very hot and we can not carry much water with us. After I filled up the bucket with grapes and pomegranates, our garden is still loaded with fruit. I remember Father's happy face when he was making wine. It was less than a year ago, but seems like a whole lifetime has passed since that happy day.

Who is going to move into our house? Who is going to pick the ripened grapes and the pomegranates? Turks? Kurds? The thought of strangers moving into my home is making me sick.

Where is our home going to be? Will we ever come back to Van?

 ## Van in This Life . . .

JULY 19, 1915

All day today the road to Igdir was covered with refugees. Cattle, donkeys, mules and the carriages full of people and household belongings, screaming babies, old men and women, all day until sunset, masses were slowly moving like a caravan with no end. Carriages and people were forming clouds of dust that were hanging dense over the city of Van.

We had to stay behind. Grandpa is the reason. This morning he told Mother that he is going to stay in Van. Oh, this stubborn Vanetsi! Nothing that we told him made him change his mind. When Mother said that she needs a man with us, Grandpa answered, "Markos comes with you and Lianoush is now stronger than I am." Araxi stepped in, "When Jevdet comes back, he is not going to spare you because you are an old man."

But Grandpa had already made up his mind and he was relentless. "Van is my home, my father's home, I am not going anywhere. When the Turk comes, I will be waiting for him on this chair, with my rifle. Turk can take my home, only after he takes me."

His behavior was odd and eccentric, but I attest that he has not gone mad. After the siege of Van was over, Grandpa bought a new rifle for himself. I have seen him cleaning it several times a week, but I am not sure he knows how to use it.

Mother was getting desperate. We were all tired of his talk. When Markos tried to tell him that we have to obey the Military Committee, Grandpa got even more agitated.

"Even if Khrimian Hairig rises from dead and comes and tells me I have to leave Van, I am not going to do it," Grandpa resisted angrily. "Van is my home, and no one can tell me to abandon it. No, no and no! I am not going anywhere from Van," he finished abruptly.

The majority of Vanetsis have already left. The Turks will be back any minute. Nothing will convince Grandpa to leave his home.

Mother will leave plenty of food and arak for him in the maran. As for us, no one is convinced that we can safely reach Russian Armenia. It is going to take us weeks and weeks to get there. Kurdish tribes and Turks are looting and killing the refugees. Cholera and typhus are taking lives every day. We have to cross the Berkri Bridge over the Arax River—that is crazy for this time of the year. To me, it is not obvious which solution is better, but we have to follow the orders of the Military Committee. Most importantly, we should try to stay together with our family, or whatever is left of it.

Tomorrow, we will join the crowds of refugees and will go on a long trip to Russian Armenia. This is my last night, at my home in Aygestan, the Garden District of Van. I am saying good-bye to my home, my childhood, my school, and my world. I don't know what will happen to us, but I swear I will never forget Van.

A thorn in Van is better than a rose somewhere else.

Mount Ararat

SEPTEMBER 14, 1915

I was sure I would never write another word in my journal. Death, tears, diseases, separation, why is all this happening to us? Why write, talk, walk, live? Within the last six months it seems like everything I had has been taken away from me. Many times I have felt that the light of life was slowly dying in me.

Until today. For the first time after I recovered from prolonged disease called typhus, I was able to walk. This morning when I looked at myself in the mirror, a stranger was staring at me. A thin face with a shaved head and dark circles around the eyes was staring at me. My long brown braids are gone. I touched my face to make sure that the reflection in the mirror is mine. I could not cry. There were no tears in my eyes. All I had inside of me was a deep, cold, dark emptiness.

Mother helped me to go outside. Mother has been through a lot of pain, but has always been there for me. Her hair is almost completely gray now and a big deep wrinkle forms a groove on her right cheek. When she smiles her eyes are wandering somewhere far away. I have not seen her crying at all. We do not talk about our family. We do not talk about the perilous march that lasted forever and comes back to me every night as a never-ending nightmare .

Erevan is the name of the town where we live now. It has narrow streets and most of the houses are made out of mud. Just like in Van, there are poplars around. Lots of poplars. Boys run around selling water and singing beautiful songs,

> *I am selling water, cold water,*
> *With my little jug,*
> *Please buy cold water from me,*
> *So I can get bread for my family.*

In Van, springs of fresh water were everywhere; here water is sold for money. I was starting to get sad again, when suddenly something happened.

Right in front of me on the horizon I saw a beautiful mountain suspended in the air from the blue sky! It had two summits, one big and one small. Both peaks were covered with snow. It looked like the most beautiful dream I had ever seen.

"What is this?" I whispered.

"This is Mount Ararat with its two peaks, Masis and Sis," I heard Mother's gentle voice.

I was puzzled. I had seen Ararat before; Markos took me to its plains once on a butterfly hunt. It looked like one big round hill. Just like any another mountain. This was different.

"This mountain looks magical," I thought out loud.

"It does," answered Mother. "We are now on the other side of Ararat, my dear." For a second, the divine image of the mountain muted the singing of the boys, in my brain. I felt the salty taste of the tears reaching my mouth.

"I am selling water, cold water," the boys were singing.

Suddenly I realized that I survived, my family survived, and we are going to live on the other side of Mount Ararat. I will always miss my Van, Aygestan, my father, Grandpa, Myranoush, Misho, my cats and much more. But this is my home now.

> *Frustration is not all life gives us and I keep hoping for hope,*
> *Who knows, maybe some day I will live again!*

> *But I still love and my heart beats, tears fall and my soul gets sick,*
> *Who knows, maybe some day I'll live?!*

> *The mountains will disappear from my memory,*
> *And my troubles will cease to nothing,*

> *Maybe I won't drown in the waves of heat,*
> *And there are always the winds to carry me away.*

> *Who knows maybe someday, I will live again and my heart will heal?*
> *But scars are always left to give the memory of nothingness. . .*

EPILOGUE

This is a story of one Armenian family, a family that had to leave their home behind in Van, the home of their ancestors, and move to Russian Armenia. This was due to massive killings and deportation of the Armenian population by the Turkish Government form 1915 to 1922. Hundreds and thousands of families had a similar destiny. Thousands of children had to go through similar experiences.

Some of the names in the story are changed, but most of the characters are based on real people.

Lianoush, whose real name was Heranoush, was chosen by fate to live a long life. After coming to Russian Armenia, she became a teacher. Big changes happened to Russian Armenia. After a short-lived independence between 1918 to 1920, Armenia was Sovietized and, in 1922, became a part of the Soviet Union as the Soviet Socialist Republic of Armenia. From 1924 until 1953, Josef Stalin spread his reign of terror over the Soviet Union. Stalin's Government killed or sent to concentration camps many innocent people, many Armenians among them. As an adult, Heranoush spent 13 years in concentration camps. Not many survived Stalin's gulags, but Heranoush did. In later years, Heranoush lived surrounded by her family, to whom she told many stories described in this book. Despite her tragic life, she was a grateful, happy, humorous, somewhat naive person who constantly shared her kindness and love with family and friends. Heranoush Beglarian was the grandmother and the great-grandmother of the authors of this book.

There are some wounds that time never mends. Even in her older years, despite pains and aches, every year on April 24 she walked for more than a mile to the Tsitsernakabert in Yerevan, a monument dedicated to the martyrs of the genocide of 1915. She bought a flower in the memory of each one of her family members killed in the massacres and added those to the thousands of flowers surrounding the eternal fire in memory of the victims.

Liavart and Ohannes died during the perilous march from Van to Yerevan.

Markar survived the march. He graduated from Yerevan State University and became a high school mathematics teacher. Soon after the World War Two started in 1941, he was drafted into the Soviet army and was sent to the battlefront. He was never heard from again.

Pailun lived a long life and cared for her two orphan granddaughters, because her only surviving daughter (Heranoush) was in the concentration camp and her son (Markar) was taken to the war.

Grandma Marina reached Russian Armenia, but died soon after. Before her death, she collected all of her belongings brought from Van and donated them to the church to help the poor and starving refugees. She was buried in Echmiadzin, not far from the Mother Church. Grandma Marina's character and her stories are mostly derived from the character of Grandma Heranoush in her older years.

Father Theos was found among the dead Armenian men shot and then disfigured by Turks; he was recognized by his wristwatch. Throughout her life, Heranoush remembered her father and his fine personality.

Araxi followed Markos (whose real names were Askhen and Gugor) to Persia and cared for his wounded shoulder. Eventually they were married, despite the disapproval of the family. They lived a long life and had two children, one of them mute and deaf.

Siranoush Tutunjian had a long, interesting life. She was a professor of biology at Yerevan State University, and throughout her life spoke beautifully about Van, wrote numerous memoirs and added color to the life of everyone she touched.

Dr. Clarence Ussher, like the rest of the Armenian population of Van, in July of 1915, was forced to leave most of his belonging in Van and go back to United States. Right before his departure from Van, he became severely ill with typhus. Unfortunately, his wife, Elizabeth Burrows Ussher who was devotedly taking care of Turks remaining in Van, also contracted typhus in a severe form. She died from it and had to be buried in Artamet. Dr. Ussher wrote a book, *The American Physician in Turkey*, that was used as one of the references for this book.

Agassi Khanjian became a famous politician and the first secretary of the Communist party of the Soviet Armenian Republic in the 1930s. He was a bright politician, dedicated to his country and his people. He became the victim of his nationalistic sentiments and was killed in 1937 by minions of Stalin. The incident was staged and publicized as suicide.

Vartan Ajemian became a famous actor and eventually the head of the National Theater of Armenia.

Panos Terlemezian, after traveling to many countries, eventually returned to Armenia and was the founder of the Armenian Academy of Art.

HISTORICAL NOTE

"Probably no people in history, not even barring the Jews, have been victims of such relentless persecution as the Armenians in the past third of a century".

—Hester Donaldson Jenkins
"Armenia and Armenians", *The National Geographic Magazine*, October, 1915

There are no Armenians in Van today. Prior to 1918, for 2500 years the presence of Armenians in Van had been continuous. For centuries, Van was the cradle of the Armenian civilization. Two preplanned massacres committed by Turkish governments eventually eliminated the entire Armenian population of Van and most of Turkey.

In the fall of 1914, Turkey entered the war as an ally of the Germans against France, Britain and the Czarist Russia. The leaders of Ottoman Turkey used the war as a pretext to execute their plan. The war provided a convenient cover to conduct a ruthless campaign against the Armenian people, seen as a major obstacle to the realization of the Young Turk aspiration to cleanse the Empire of its Christian Population.

In February of 1915, Jevdet Bey, a man known for his despicable cruelty, became the newly appointed governor of Van. He initiated the deportations and mass killings of the population of the Armenian villages in the area. Several Armenian party leaders were summoned as mediators or given governmental tasks, but were treacherously brutally murdered. That was how Jevdet Bey was trying to eliminate the leadership in order to be able to easily deal with the rest of the population.

The three parties united to defend the whole Armenian population of Van. The Military Counsel headed by Aram Manukyan and

Armenak Ekarian, leaders of two parties (Dashnak and Armenakan), led the Armenian population's defense against the many times larger and better armed Turkish army; it lasted 26 days, from April 7th until May 3rd. It was a heroic battle of a nation that refused to be exterminated. The regular Turkish army, joined with well-armed and violent Kurdish tribes, had more advanced ammunition and better positions. Armenians of Van showed a heroic resistance. The siege of Van came to an end only when the Turks realized that the Russian army was approaching and began to flee. Van was liberated, but was left in ruins. For a short time, Armenians were rewarded with freedom and started to repair their homes and the damage of the furious battle. However, Russians were called back by the Czarist government at the end of July; Armenians of Van were ordered to pack their belongings, abandon their homes and set out to follow the army to the Caucasus.

Armenians returned several more times to Van until 1918, but trapped in big political games practiced by the allied powers and the Bolshevik government of Russia, they had to leave their homeland and lose it forever. Towards the end of the war, in an attempt to end the war at any price, Lenin signed a treaty with the Germans on March 3, 1918, known as Brest-Litovsk Treaty. In accordance with this treaty, Russia withdrew its army from eastern parts of Turkey, relinquishing Kars, Ardahan, Ani and Mount Ararat, the sacred mountain of the Armenians, to the Turks. Prior to WWI, these lands were under Russian control. Working with their German allies, Enver and Talaat had been able to return lost territories and gain more by annexing the territories of Russian Armenia.

The defense of Van was presented as insurgence against the Ottoman government that had to be crushed. The fifty-five thousand slaughtered Armenians in the Province of Van were falsely reported as Muslims who had been massacred by Christian Armenians. And so, generations of Turks are misled in their own history.

The majority of the Armenian population of Turkey had a more tragic fate. Before the horrific events of 1915, about two million Armenians lived throughout Ottoman Turkey. The story of Van is one of the rare ones, when Armenians actually fought the organized Turkish troops. This was possible because the civil population in Van was predominantly Armenian. In the majority of Turkish provinces, big cities, and even in the other six Armenian Provinces, the Armenian population wasn't as concentrated. Armenian leaders and men underwent massive arrests and executions; many men were killed in front of their families in their homes. Defenseless Armenian women, children and old men were taken from their homes and deported to the southern desert to die. That was the cheapest and most convenient way for the Ottomans to get rid of Armenians and take their homes and wealth. In many cases, they could even claim the life insurance policies of the perished Armenians.

The Ottoman Turkish government methodically carried out the deportation and mass murders in cities, towns and villages populated by Armenians: Van, Erzerum, Sivas, Ceasarea, Adana, Ardahan, Kharpert, Marash, Bayazet, Malatsia, Zeytoun, Sasun, Diarbekir, Aintab, Urfa, Bitlis, Kars, Mush, Smyrna and many others. Most of the Armenians throughout the world will recognize one of these cities as the home of their grandparents.

One and one-half million Armenians were killed in Turkey from 1915 to 1922. Not all of them were brutally murdered; many of them died from diseases, starvation or dehydration during the marches through Turkey toward the Syrian Desert of Deir Zor. Many women committed suicide trying to save themselves from Turkish hands. Many young Armenian children and women were forcibly converted into Islam and were "Turkicized." There are multiple documents with numerous facts presented by foreign diplomats, and reports from witnesses about the horrors that the Armenian population of Turkey had to endure. Many Armenian survivors like the Vanetsis took refuge in Russian Armenia. War-torn Armenians declared their independence on the small corner of their historic homeland. But freedom was short lived. The newly independent Republic of Armenia fell victim to the Bolshevik-Kemalist conspiracy. Armenia was "Sovietized," and even this small country was mutilated and lands were given to Turkey and Azerbaijan.

The Turkish Governments of 1894 to 1922 committed the Armenian genocide, not the Turkish people. Despite the deceiving anti-Armenian propaganda by the Government, many Turks and Kurds protected their neighbors and refused to participate in the massacre of Armenians.

As a result of the genocide of 1915, Armenians were spread throughout the world, and frequently, were described by the older generation of different countries as the "starving Armenians."

Every year, Armenians all over the world acknowledge April 24 as a day of remembrance of the victims of genocide. April 24 has been chosen because on that day many famous Armenian leaders, writers and poets were arrested in Constantinopole. They were either killed in prisons or sent into exile to the interior of the empire, many murdered along the way.

Mustafa Kemal, known as Ataturk, father of the Turks and founder of modern Turkey, continued the anti-Armenian policy of his predecessors. He drove out the Armenian refugees who dared to return to their homes after the fall of the empire and claimed, "No Armenian provinces have ever existed in Turkey." The denial continues, unfortunately, until today.

The Turkish government has not acknowledged the atrocities committed by the Young Turk government against the Armenian population of Ottoman Turkey. The perished Armenians are called a "normal" consequence of WWI. The Turkish Republic today supports the view of its founder, and not only continues to deny the genocide of 1.5 million Armenians, but also persists to ignore the 2500 years of Armenian presence on that land. The fortresses and ruins of the Urartian Kingdom are proudly shown as a historic heritage of contemporary Turkey. The 2500-year continuous presence of the Armenians in the same area is completely disregarded. Hundreds of Christian Armenian churches are decaying, sitting half ruined, the Armenian writings are erased, crosses are demolished and history is rewritten. Only few unique Armenian Churches remain erect as an eternal monument of the Armenian civilization of Van and other parts of historic Armenia.

Today, Van, with its natural beauty and historic monuments, is a tourist attraction. In the fierce fight of 1915 between the Armenian defenders and Turkish troops, the Old City of Van was completely destroyed, beyond restoration. On the place of the old City, there is a grassy land with a couple of minarets and the base of an Armenian Church. The Urartian Citadel and the Rock of Van are there to remind us of the glory of that ancient city.

The new Van has risen in the place of old Aygestan. The population of today's Van consists of Kurds and Turks.

After the collapse of Soviet Union, in 1991 Armenia regained independence. Today, Armenia is a small, landlocked country bordering Turkey, Iran, Georgia and Azerbaijan. Yerevan is the capital of the modern Armenia and is located on the plains of Ararat Valley. With the first rays of sun, every morning the Armenians of Yerevan see the beautiful, Holy, Mount Ararat. Mount Ararat, is geographically located in Turkey, but remains the symbol of the Fatherland for the Armenians of Armenia and all over the world.

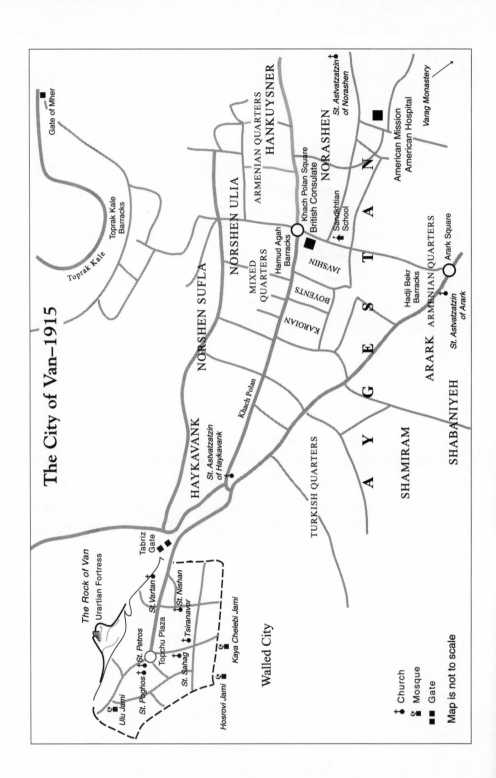

The City of Van–1915

Gate of Mher

Toprak Kale Barracks

Toprak Kale

NORSHEN ULIA

NORSHEN SUFLA

ARMENIAN QUARTERS

HANKUYSNER

NORASHEN

St. Astvatzatzin of Norashen

American Mission
American Hospital

Varag Monastery

MIXED QUARTERS

Khach Polan Square
British Consulate

Sandkhtian School

Hamud Agah Barracks

JAVSHIN

BOYENTS

KAROIAN

N

T

S

E

G

Y

A

Hadji Bekr Barracks

Arark Square

St. Astvatzatzin of Arark

ARARK

ARMENIAN QUARTERS

SHAMIRAM

SHABANIYEH

Khach Polan

HAYKAVANK

St. Astvatzatzin of Haykavank

TURKISH QUARTERS

The Rock of Van
Urartian Fortress

Tabriz Gate

St. Vartan

St. Nishan

Topchu Plaza

Tsiranavor

St. Petros

St. Peghos

St. Sahag

Kaya Chelebi Jami

Ulu Jami

Hosrovi Jami

Walled City

† Church
ç Mosque
■ Gate

Map is not to scale

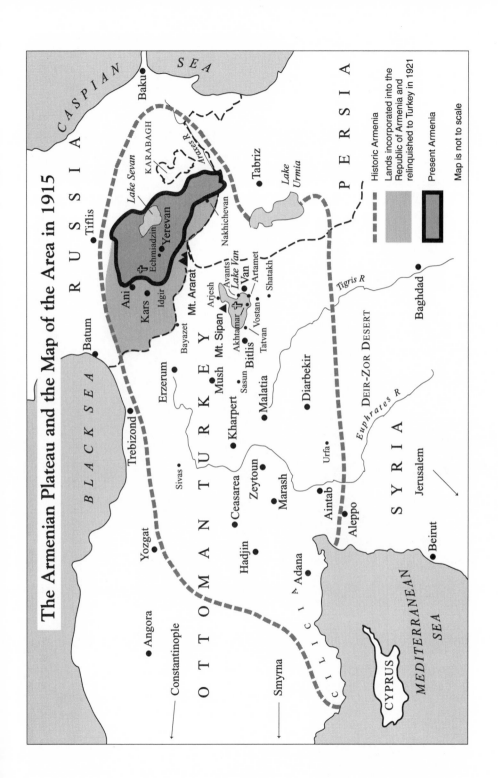

The Armenian Plateau and the Map of the Area in 1915

Historic Armenia

Lands incorporated into the Republic of Armenia and relinquished to Turkey in 1921

Present Armenia

Map is not to scale

CASPIAN SEA

Baku

RUSSIA

PERSIA

Tiflis

KARABAGH

Araxes R.

Lake Sevan

Tabriz

Lake Urmia

Echmiadzin

Yerevan

Nakhichevan

Ani

Kars

Idgir

Mt. Ararat

Bayazet

Batum

Arjesh

Avants

Lake Van

Van

Artamet

Shatakh

Tigris R.

Baghdad

TURKEY

Mush

Sasun

Akhtamar

Vostan

Tatvan

Mt. Sipan

Bitlis

Malatia

Diarbekir

DEIR-ZOR DESERT

Erzerum

Euphrates R.

Trebizond

Kharpert

BLACK SEA

Sivas

Ceasarea

Zeytoun

Marash

Urfa

SYRIA

Jerusalem

Yozgat

Aintab

Aleppo

Hadjin

Beirut

OTTOMAN

Angora

Adana

CILICIA

Constantinople

Smyrna

CYPRUS

MEDITERRANEAN SEA

The survivors of the Kosparian–Beglarian family

Seated, left to right: Markar, Pailun, and Heranoush (Lianoush). *Standing:* Askhen (Araxi).

REFERENCES

The following books were used to illustrate the historical background of the book.

Balakian, Peter
2003

The Burning Tigris. New York: HarperCollins Publishers.

Hewsen, Robert H.
2001

Armenia A Historic Atlas. Chicago (Printed in Italy): The University of Chicago Press.

Hichens, Robert
1913

The Near East. New York: The Century Company.

Hovannisian, Richard G.
2000

Armenian Van/Vaspurakan. Costa Mesa, CA: Mazda Publishers, Inc.

Jenkins, Hester Donaldson
1915

Armenia and Armenians. Washington, DC: The National Geographic Magazine.

Keorkizian, Ver. A.
1965

The Heroic Struggle of Vaspurakan. Beirut: Atlas Publishing (Armenian).

Mahari, Gurgen
1966

Airvogh Aygestanner (Burning Gardens). Yerevan: Hayastan (Armenian).

Ussher, Clarence D.
2002

An American Physician in Turkey. London: Sterndale Classics.

ABOUT THE AUTHORS

Mariam and Elize Manoukian are mother and daughter, who live in Mountain View, California, with the rest of the family, Jerry, Gregory and two cats. Mariam Avakian grew up in Yerevan, Armenia, and now is a medical doctor in private practice with her husband, Jerry. Elize is currently in fifth grade and loves to read and write poetry. They all love to write and compose stories.